DOORWAY TO THE BIBLE

Creation

From International Publishing Co., Ltd.

"IN the beginning God . . ." (Genesis 1:1)

THESE are the opening words of the Bible. No more profound yet simple statement could be made. From the dateless past, even from all eternity, God has been, and always will be.

"In the beginning God created the heavens and the earth." By the command of the Almighty the universe of things—the planets, stars, constellations, the earth, and then mankind came into being. The Bible adds: "Through faith we understand that the worlds were framed by the word of God, so that things which are seen were not made of things which do appear."

God has revealed Himself to us in his works (the universe), in his Word (the Bible), and finally in his Son, the Lord Jesus Christ. All of God's revelation is inexpressibly wonderful and beautiful as we can see in our lovely world, in the sun, moon, and stars; also in the Bible which is presented in the Book of Life; and especially in the Savior, the Altogether Lovely One.

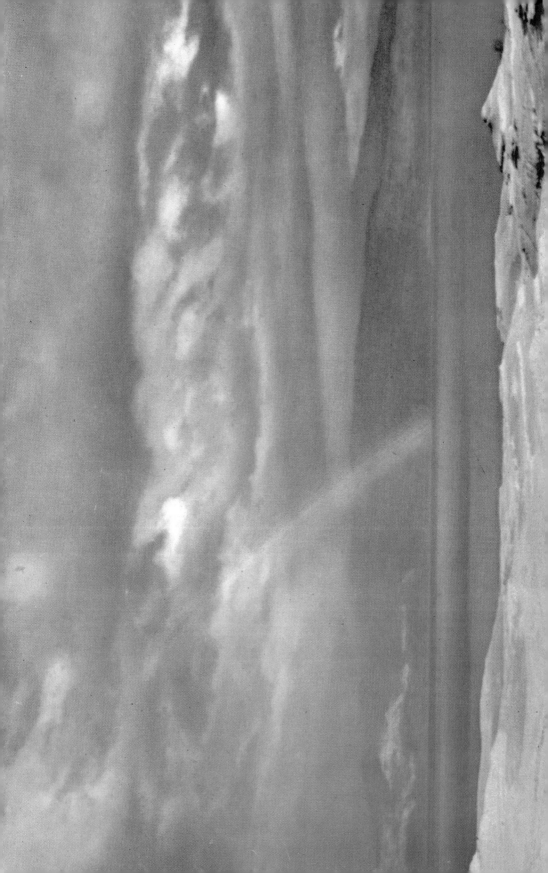

VOLUME 1

*DOORWAY TO
THE BIBLE*

THE
BOOK of LIFE

ARRANGED AND EDITED BY

NEWTON M. HALL, A.M., D.D., *Pastor and Christian Educator,*
Author of Civic Righteousness and Civic Pride

IRVING F. WOOD, Ph.D., D.D. *Professor of Religion and Bible,*
Author of The Spirit of God in Biblical Literature

Joint Authors of The Bible Story; Early Days of Israel; Days of the Kings
of Israel; Adult Bible Classes and How to Teach Them

JOHN RUDIN &
COMPANY, INC.
Chicago

ACKNOWLEDGMENTS

We gratefully acknowledge our indebtedness to the following for valued editorial counsel and assistance: V. Raymond Edman, Ph.D., L.L.D., President, Wheaton College; Paul E. Kretzmann, Ph.D., D.D.; the late George L. Robinson, Ph.D., D.D.; Merrill C. Tenney, Ph.D.; the late Professor Robert L. Cooke, Ed.D.; John Luchies, Th.D.; Professor Kenneth S. Kantzer, Ph.D.; all distinguished and devout Biblical scholars, teachers and authors; Louise Rock, Children's Religious Book Editor; Moody Press for *Stories of Hymns We Love;* Dr. Wm. S. McBirnie; Lewis Bayles Paton, D.D., Hartford Theological Seminary; Edgar J. Goodspeed, Ph.D.; Elihu Grant, Ph.D., Professor of Biblical Literature, Haverford College; Henry Thatcher Fowler, D.D., Professor of Biblical Literature, Brown University; Mr. and Mrs. W. A. Pottenger; Mr. Charles F. H. Crathern, Jr.; the American Passion Play of Bloomington, Illinois, and Bess Hibarger for helping to assemble Passion Play pictures; The Pilgrim Press; Edwin Markham; Houghton, Mifflin and Company; Fleming H. Revell & Company; The Abingdon Press; British Broadcasting Corporation, Copyright, London, W. 1.

We make grateful acknowledgment to the following Art Galleries for permission to use their pictures: Metropolitan Art Museum of New York; British Museum of London; Boston Museum of Fine Art; National Gallery, London; National Tate Gallery, London; The Louvre, Paris, France; National Museum, Naples, Italy; National Gallery, Dresden, Germany; Galleria Ambrosiana, Milan, Italy; The Art Institute of Chicago; Curtis & Cameron, Incorporated.

For special contributions by Professor Robert Seneca Smith; Clara Bodman Hawks; Mrs. Louise Hall Tharp; Cecilia Rudin; Helen Rudin; and Frances Olcott; and many others for their help, the publishers here wish to extend grateful and sincere appreciation.

The pictures by James J. Tissot are reproductions of original paintings of the "New Testament" at the Brooklyn Museum, New York, and of the "Old Testament" at the Jewish Museum, New York. Permission for use by John H. Eggers Publications, New York, who have exclusive publication rights. These photos, and others, were taken by Three Lions, Inc., New York. Other photos in color are used by permission of International Publishing Co., Ltd., Jerusalem, and Wide World Photos.

INTRODUCTION

THE Bible is the greatest book in the world. It is the divinely inspired record of the dealings of God with men through the centuries. The Bible is not like an ordinary book; its importance may not be overestimated. To be of any value to the individual and to the world, however, the book must be read. The aim of the editors of THE BOOK OF LIFE is to get the Bible read, to help people to read it and to understand it, to appreciate it and to enjoy it. "Whither shall we go?" said the disciple of Jesus; "Thou has the words of Eternal Life." THE BOOK OF LIFE, "the words of eternal life"; these are not simply in the Bible, they are the Bible. It must be remembered that these words of eternal life were not all originally in a book. Some were written down, but almost the entire Bible was spoken before it was written. It was spoken by men of spirituality, of originality, of power, men who walked with God: the prophets who spoke with passionate earnestness the great messages of God; Jesus, from whose lips the words of eternal life came in their original freshness and grace and charm; Paul, who spoke to all men, in all places in the wide Roman Empire. The later generations are at a very great disadvantage because they must read what was once powerfully spoken. In the ordinary printed Bible, the background is missing. The personality of the speaker, the country of the speaker, the hills of Galilee, the streets of Jerusalem, the great nations which imperilled the life of the Hebrew people: Egypt, Assyria, Babylon, Persia; the later empires, Greece and Rome, the scene of the spread of Christianity—these are missing. It greatly adds to our appreciation and understanding of the sermons of Amos and Isaiah to know something of the great empires which were the foes of Israel and to understand the social conditions of the times.

The editors of THE BOOK OF LIFE have done just this! They have used every possible device and piece of historical information to make the Bible a real and living book. They have not added anything to the Bible—no man can do that.

7

They have simply attempted to restore the conditions, to illustrate the sacred text, to make the Bible live again for this generation.

The editors do not claim to have done anything entirely new or original. Illustrated Bibles have been in existence from the earliest times. Many of the best editions of Luther's day and of Puritan times were illustrated and annotated. The editors claim simply to have done this important work for our own day and generation, for the children and the men and women of today, the earnest devout people who know the value of the Bible, who long to possess it and to have their children possess it. To the great army of such men and women, to the young people of our country, THE BOOK OF LIFE is dedicated.

The Bible text is the "Authorized," "King James" version—the best reading version of the Bible, the best to convey to the mind the splendid and stately imagery of the original translation of the days of King James. The language has changed somewhat since those days and a vocabulary of obsolete words and phrases, with the important changes made by the "new versions" is provided.

THE BOOK OF LIFE is unique in that it provides a clarity and understanding in reading the Bible not found in any other work.

1. LARGE TYPE AND FULL LINES. The Bible is usually printed with small type and narrow, double columns which prevent clear and easy reading. In designing THE BOOK OF LIFE, the editors and publishers consulted reading authorities in order to select and use the right size of type for various age groups—the proper length of line and the amount of white space required for the most restful and continuous reading. Consequently, THE BOOK OF LIFE can be read by the young and old with a minimum of eyestrain. Perhaps no book in the world contains more conversation than the Bible—and yet there are no quotation marks in the average Bible. By contrast, quotation marks are used throughout the entire nine Volumes of THE BOOK OF LIFE.

2. THOUGHT DIVISIONS. In the Bible, arbitrary chapter and verse divisions often interrupt both thought and continuity —making it difficult to read. Here, in THE BOOK OF LIFE,

each story is given a heading and thought divisions are used instead of verse and chapter divisions which really were never in the original manuscripts. However, references to chapter and verse are provided at the end of each section so that one may know exactly what portion of the Bible he is reading. Selections of the same general literary type are grouped together. Each Volume is sub-divided into periods convenient for reading and study. Each section is provided with questions and notes.

3. EASY-TO-FOLLOW COLORED MAPS. Bibles generally contain complicated maps with many names in very small type. Growing children—and even adults—find them hard to understand. These maps are usually found in the back of the Bible—which make them inconvenient to use. THE BOOK OF LIFE, in contrast, has "on-the-spot" colored maps drawn to illustrate the immediate and accompanying story or text. All the way through the Bible, these maps are right where they are needed.

4. NEARLY SIXTEEN HUNDRED PICTURES. It is believed that no work on the Bible has ever brought together a collection of pictures as educational and stimulating as those in THE BOOK OF LIFE. They give the background against which the Bible heroes, prophets, and saints walked and spoke —lived and died. First of all, there are hundreds of photographs which enable the reader to visualize the land as the Bible Story unfolds. Many are geographical pictures, illustrating the actual scenery of the Holy Land and the other countries with which the Bible narrative makes contact. Others are Archaeological pictures. The spade of the explorer has been the great instrument for the recovery of data confirming and illustrating Biblical material.

There are hundreds of great Master Paintings to illustrate the text, and many of these are in glorious color. They come from the greatest Art Galleries of the world. THE BOOK OF LIFE contains a complete history of Christian Art from the first rude symbols of the catacombs down to the work of modern English, French, and American Masters.

5. HISTORY AND RELATED THINGS ARE PUT IN CHRONOLOGICAL ORDER. The Editors have arranged

THE BOOK OF LIFE for clear, understandable reading by putting history and related things in chronological order—just the way they happened. Many Bible readers are confused and do not know, for example, where to start reading the life of Moses—inasmuch as there is no Book in the Bible entitled "Moses." Incidents in the life of Moses may be found in four Books of the Bible—Exodus, Leviticus, Numbers, Deuteronomy —and Bible scholars know that it would take hours of study in order to piece the narrative together in its proper sequence. THE BOOK OF LIFE presents the Story of Moses in a thrilling, unbroken narrative—covering 173 pages, entitled "Moses the Emancipator." In THE BOOK OF LIFE, one may read the lives of all Bible characters in the same interesting and fascinating manner.

6. TWO THOUSAND EXPLANATORY NOTES OCCUR THROUGHOUT THE TEXT. The text of THE BOOK OF LIFE is tremendously enhanced by the truly fascinating introductory and explanatory notes—most helpful in understanding the Bible text. They are historical, geographical, archaeological, biographical, and educational. They are not doctrinal or denominational. There are many names of characters in the Bible that are not well known. It is helpful to have "thumbnail sketches" to describe these people and put the reader "in the know." Then, one need not read on wondering who they are or how they fit into the unfolding story. And, it is such a "time saver" to have this background information at one's fingertips. They take the "search" out of Bible "research" for the reader, and make the Bible even more fascinating.

And further, there are many great poems and hymns of Bible subjects added throughout the Volumes in appropriate places. Then, too, there are many references throughout THE BOOK OF LIFE to material found in different Volumes of the set. These are indicated in this way: 3:125, which means that the material may be found in Volume 3, page 125.

To reveal the Bible with reverent scholarship, with dramatic effect as a living Book—without sectarian or personal bias— has been the devoted purpose of both Editors and Publishers in building THE BOOK OF LIFE.

PREFACE

DOORWAY TO THE BIBLE" is planned to lead girls and boys to an understanding and love of the Bible. The Bible is primarily an adult book. But there are many Bible stories which children can understand and love. There are many Bible truths which children can know and live. This book is a doorway leading into the Bible.

BIBLE STORIES

The Bible stories in this volume are based directly on the accounts as they appear in the Bible. The facts in the Bible record are followed carefully. Background description, conversation, and "what could have happened" are added to make the story more meaningful to today's child. But the basic truth of the Bible narrative is retained in each Bible story.

As children read or listen to these Bible stories, the Bible will be opening up to them in a way that they can understand. These stories have been chosen as ones which have special appeal to children. They are told in the everyday language that children speak today.

CHARACTER-BUILDING STORIES

The "present-day" stories in this volume are "character-building" stories. Their purpose is to lead the child to live and think more as Jesus would want him to.

The basic themes for these stories were chosen after much study of children's character development needs in our society today. Children have many problems of behavior, and of mental and spiritual adjustment. These stories were written especially to meet their needs and help them overcome their problems.

Perhaps your child has a behavior problem. Instead of saying, "Don't do that," or "Don't do this," or "What am I going to do with you?" read an appropriate story to him. Let the message of the story speak for itself.

Perhaps your child needs help in understanding the world around him, or in understanding himself. As he reads these stories, he will find some of the answers he is searching for.

PRAYERS

The prayers in this volume are chosen especially for children. They may want to learn some of the prayers. They will want to read others.

As boys and girls become familiar with these prayers, they will discover a greater knowledge of what prayer is. They will find enriched blessing in their own prayer life.

FOR CHILDREN OF ALL AGES

This volume is planned for the growing needs of children of various ages.

For very little children, as young as two years, this book is a "read-aloud" book. With these small children, you may be just starting a story when a little hand turns the page. Simply go on to the next story, or merely talk about the pictures. Even though they do not listen to a story all the way through, these little ones will think of this as a book especially for them.

Pre-schoolers will enjoy listening to the stories, too. But they will listen to the whole story and often ask to hear a favorite story again and again. As you read to your pre-school child, he will become familiar with Bible stories even before he can read them himself. The stories in this volume will be understandable to him because of their simplicity.

The child who is just starting school, in his first and second year, will find a special joy in reading these stories. The first part of the book is planned just for this "beginning reader." The words are chosen primarily from first and second grade word-lists. The "beginning reader" can read these stories himself, with little or no help from Mother and Father.

The "beginning reader" finds a tremendous excitement in being able to read a word—a phrase—a whole sentence, all by himself. When he can read an entire story, he is thrilled almost beyond words. The stories are short, so he will not become discouraged. This volume gives the "beginning reader" stories of

12

the highest type which he can read himself. As he does, he will have the double pleasure of reading Bible stories himself and of learning more about God's Book. He will read about present-day boys and girls just like the boys and girls he knows.

The child who is a little beyond the "beginning reader" stage, but not yet able to read the newspaper easily, will find the second section of this volume just right for him. Very few of the words are harder than a third grade reading level. These "in-between readers" will read of people in Bible days and of girls and boys today—all who learned about God's way.

The "in-between reader" needs spiritual guidance, but seldom finds it in his reading material. It is here for him in words he can read and understand.

The older child—the girl or boy who can read quite well—will enjoy this volume, too. The stories are short, so he can read them quickly. The vocabulary is simple, so he can read them easily. And he may enjoy reading the stories aloud to a younger brother or sister.

Even if there are no children in your home, keep this volume on hand. It will be ideal for entertaining small visitors, who will be delighted to find something in your home just for them.

This book is for all children. Don't put it up on a high shelf to keep it clean. Don't put it away for special occasions only. Keep it in a place where the children can reach it themselves. To be of value to a child, a book must be handled, looked at, and read.

This book is for your child. It will introduce him to the Bible, enrich his life, and lead him in God's way.

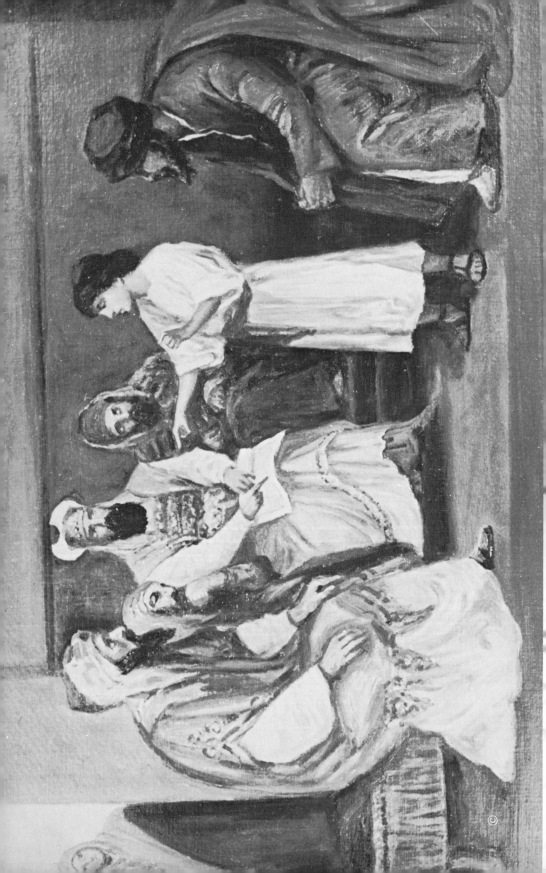

CONTENTS

Volume One

MY BIBLE PRIMER

Page

15

JESUS AMONG THE DOCTORS
A painting by Robert Leinweber

MY BIBLE READER

Note: The Bible stories in this volume are based on the Scripture references listed with the Bible story titles.

Infant in Swaddling Clothes

By Andrea della Robbia (1435-1525)
Medallion on Façade of the Foundling's Hospital,
Florence, Italy

FOURTEEN of these world-famous medallions deco-
rate the façade of the Hospital of St. Mary of the
Foundlings in Florence. They are placed in the spaces
between the curves of arches along a raised porch. Ten
of the medallions are the original work of Andrea della
Robbia and were set in place in about the 1470's or
1480's. This figure shows a bambino (baby) with both
arms extended as if appealing for mercy, and is full of
the charm and childhood grace for which Andrea and
his uncle, Luca della Robbia, were so famous. It is made
of glazed terra-cotta.

Andrea della Robbia received the best of training as
a sculptor under his uncle, Luca, and in the field of
glazed terra-cotta was his natural successor. Andrea
was born in Florence and worked there for the greater
part of his life. From his shop works were transported
to all parts of Italy. The business was a flourishing one
and from the outset of his career Andrea's success was
so great that he could not supply the demand without
considerable assistance. Of his sons, five followed their
father's profession. The della Robbia figures were the
most popular of their day and were used everywhere.
Most of them are in relief, that is slightly raised figures,
such as this delightful bambino. The elder della Robbias,
Luca and Andrea, used colors sparingly, blue and white
being the most usual combination. In the later produc-
tions of the school many more colors and numerous
accessories such as animals, flowers and fruits were used
and the results were not nearly as attractive or artistic.
Andrea's compositions, as we can see from this illustra-
tion, were essentially decorative and full of refinement
and grace. This medallion is thirty-nine inches in
diameter.

MY
BIBLE
PRIMER

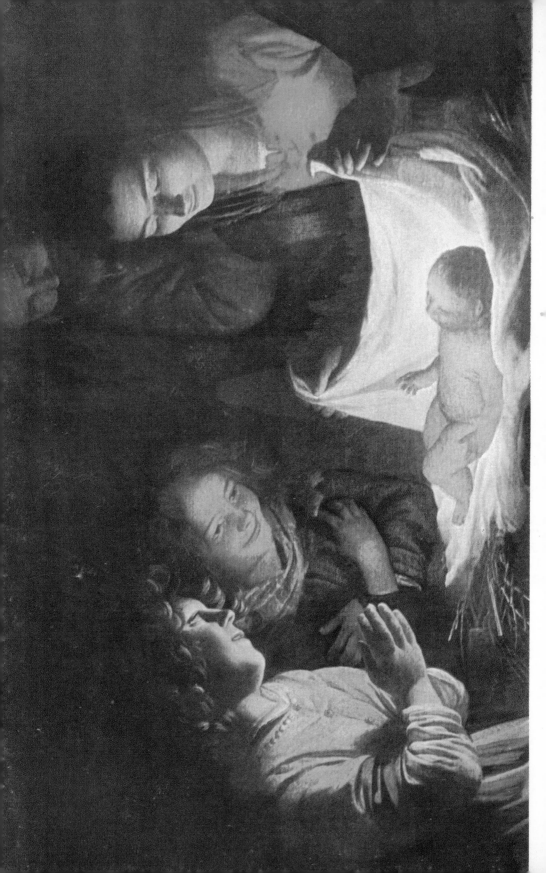

Easy
Reading
Stories

THE NEW HOUSE

"What a fine house!" said Billy.

"It is our new house,"
said Father.

"Soon we will live in it."

"How did we get our new house?"
asked Sally.

"Men built it," said Father.

"They used wood to make
the walls," said Mother.

"They used wood to make
the floors and the doors, too,"
said Billy.

"Where did they get the wood?"
asked Sally.

"Wood comes from trees,"
said Billy.
"And God made the trees."
"Our house is made from trees,"
said Sally. Then she laughed.
"Our house is made from trees,"
she said. "But it does not
look like a tree."
Billy laughed too.
"No," he said.
"It does not look like a tree.
But our new house
will make me think of a tree.
And trees make me think of God."
"God gave us trees," said Sally.
"And God gave us our new house."

MOVING DAY

" 'Moving Day' today !" said Billy.
Ring-ring went the doorbell.
Two men had come. They said,
"We are here to help you move."
The men looked around.
They picked up a big table.
They took it out to their truck.
Then the men took the beds.
They moved out everything.
Last of all, the men rolled up
the rugs and took them out.

Then Billy and his family rode
in the car to the new house.
Father said, "Let us go in.
Into our new house that God
gave us."

BILLY AND HIS FAMILY

One day, Father said,
"We will all work in the yard."
Sally said, "I like it when we
work together."
Father cut the grass and raked.
Mother worked in the garden.
Billy put grass in a basket.
Sally helped all of them.
Their dog Taffy barked and played.
When they were tired and hot
Mother brought out a cold drink.
How good it tasted!
"Our house is fun to live in,"
said Sally.
"It is fun because our family
works together," said Father.
"I'm glad God gave me my house,"
said Billy. "And I'm very glad
that God gave me my family."

FRIENDS

"Can my friend Ray stay with us
all night?" asked Billy.
"His father is sick."
Sally said, "Ray can not make
any noise at his house."
"Of course, your friend
may stay with us," said Mother.

Billy ran to Ray's house.

Soon Billy and Ray came back.

Ray's little dog, Fox, came too.

Ray stayed for three days.

Then his father was better.

"I'm glad that I could stay
with you," said Ray.

"You are my friend," said Billy.

Father smiled. "God wants us
to help our friends," he said.

GOD PLANS FOR DAY

Jack and his sister Mary lived
in another house nearby.
One morning, Jack said to Mary,
"Wake up, sleepyhead!"
He opened the window wide.
"It is daylight," he said.
Mary sat up and rubbed her eyes.
"I can see the garden," she said,
"and the colors of the flowers."
"And you can see Mickey, too,"
said Jack.
"He is not a sleepyhead."
Mary said, "I like to run and
skip when it is daylight."
Jack said, "And I like
to play with Mickey."
Mary smiled. She said,
"I am glad that God planned
to give us daylight."

GOD PLANS FOR NIGHT

"I wish it was morning," said
Mary. She looked at the moon
in the dark sky, and said,
"Then I could play some more."
Jack laughed. "Could you play
all day and all night, too?"
"Yes," she said.
"I could play with my doll."
She yawned a big yawn.

"The moon is not as bright
as the sun," she said.
"If the moon was bright
like the sun," said Jack,
"it would be hard to go to sleep."
Mary yawned again, then said,
"I am glad God planned the night.
I am sleepy now."
Jack watched the moon
as it went behind a cloud.
"Good-night, God," he said.
"I am going to sleep now, too."

THE PINK TREE

"A pink tree!" said Helen.

"Let's play house under it."

So Helen and Bobby played house.

But one day, little Bobby said,

"Our tree is a green tree now!"

"It is green now," said Helen,

"because this is summer."

So they played house

under their green tree.

Then one morning, Bobby said,

"Look at our tree!

It is brown and red now."

"This is fall," said Helen.

"Leaves get brown and red now."

One day, Bobby said,

"The leaves are blowing away."

Soon the tree had no leaves.

"Our tree looks sad," he said.

"This is winter," said Helen.

"Spring will come again."

"Will God make our tree pink
in the spring?" asked Bobby.

"Yes," said Helen. "God will
give us our pink tree then."

BREAKFAST

"I am so hungry !" said Susan.

"I am hungry, too," said Peter.

"I am glad that we eat breakfast

as soon as we get up."

Father laughed. He said,

"Eat a big breakfast, Peter.

Then you will not need lunch."

"Oh yes I will," said Peter.

"I will eat a big lunch."

They bowed their heads while

Susan prayed,

"Thank You, God, for our food."

Then Father asked,

"Where do we get our breakfast?"

"I know," said Susan. "I know.

It comes from the kitchen.

Mother cooks it on the stove."

THE STORE

Father said, "Every morning
Mother cooks our breakfast.
But where does it come from?"
Peter said, "From the store.
Yesterday I went to the store.
I bought milk and bread,
and many other things."

Susan asked,
"But where does the man
in the store get the food?"
"From a farmer," said Peter.
"Oh, yes," said Susan. "I know.
Milk comes from cows."
Peter said, "And eggs
are laid by chickens."
"That's right," said Father.
"Now we know where food
comes from," said Peter.
"Yes," said Susan. "From farms."
Peter said, "And God made
the farms."

THE YELLOW FIELD

"See the yellow field,"
said Susan.
They were riding past a farm.
"You will eat some of that
for breakfast," said Father.
Susan laughed. She said,
"I do not eat yellow grass."
"That is grain," said Father.
"They use grain to make flour."
Susan said, "Mother has flour.
It does not taste good."
Peter said, "I know what people
do with flour. They make bread."
Susan laughed again. She said,
"Yes, I eat bread at breakfast."
"God plans for farmers and sun
and rain to make grain grow,"
said Peter. "So that we can have
bread for breakfast."

A DRINK OF WATER

"I am so thirsty," said Jimmy.
He went to the kitchen
and got a glassful of cold water.
He drank it all.
"That was good!" he said.
"I like water when I'm thirsty."
"So does Pal," said Kathy.
Pal was drinking the water
in his water dish.

"We need water to live."
said Jimmy.
"And so do dogs and rabbits
and horses," said Kathy.
"And flowers and trees, too,"
said Mother.
"But how does the water get
into our house?" asked Kathy.
"It goes under the ground
in big pipes," said Jimmy.
"It comes from lakes and
rivers," said Mother.
"How does the water get
into the lakes?" asked Kathy.
Jimmy thought a minute.
"Rain falls into the lakes," he said.

RAIN

"It is dark out," said Kathy,
"and it is not night."
Jimmy said, "It will rain."
"I wanted to go out," she said.
"Why does it rain today?"
"To give us water," said Jimmy.
"Trees and flowers need water
to grow," said Mother.
"The rabbits and squirrels
need water, too," said Jimmy.

Kathy watched the rain.
Later she said,
"The rain has stopped."
"See the rainbow."
said Mother.
"The rainbow helps us
remember that God takes care
of us," said Jimmy.
Kathy smiled. "I did not like
the rain when I wanted to go
out," she said, "but now I am
glad it rained."

GOD TAKES CARE OF US

"Why do I need God to take
care of me, Father?" asked Tommy.
"I have you and Mother."
Father said, "God has helpers
to help Him with His work."
"Yes," said Mother. "We help
God by taking care of you.

So we are God's helpers."

"I did not know that," said Beth.

"When you take care of us,
you are helping God."

Tommy thought a minute. He said,

"Beth and I are helpers too.

We help take care of the baby."

Beth sat on Father's lap.

"God planned the best way
to take care of us," she said.

"He gave mothers and fathers
to boys and girls."

WHAT GOD MADE

"I wish I could see God,"
said Linda. "Where is He?"
"God is everywhere," said Fred.
Linda said, "I cannot see Him,
but I know He made everything."
Fred asked, "How many things
can you see that God has made?"
"Sun and trees," said Linda.
"Flowers," said little Jane,
holding some she had picked.
"Sky and hills," called John,
standing between two trees.
"Grass and stones," said Ann
from behind another tree.
"Dogs, too," said Fred.
"God made many, many things."
"I cannot see God," said Linda,
"but I can see the things
that He has made."

WHERE GOD IS

"God made everything,"
said Linda. "He made dogs
and cats and ducks."
"And people, too," said Fred.
"People can do things that
animals cannot," said Linda.
"Yes, people are special,"
said Fred.
"People can love other people,"
said Linda. "People can think
and they can talk."

Linda and Fred walked slowly
down the hill.
It was quiet all around.
They walked along the stream.
They saw a boy fishing.
Everything was very quiet.
Linda shut her eyes.
In a minute she opened them.
She spoke softly. She said,
"I cannot see God. But when
I close my eyes, I can feel
that He is beside me."
"God made us," said Fred.
"And we can love Him."
"God is everywhere,"
said Linda. "I'm glad that
He is with me all the time."

HOME BY THE SEA

Very early every morning,
Father went out in his boat.
He was a fisherman.
Dick waved to him as he left.
"Mother," Dick said one day,
"Father owns the house and boat,
but who owns the sea?"
Mother said, "God owns the sea."
"God made the sea," said Dick,
"so it belongs to Him,
and He is here with us."
Every afternoon Dick watched
for Father's boat to come home.
He knew the boat a long way off.
Every night, after Father
came home, Dick watched
the light from the lighthouse.
"I'm glad I live by the sea,"
he said. "God is always here."

HOME IN THE MOUNTAINS

"We are going to visit
Uncle Ralph's home
in the mountains," said Mother.
Dick had never seen a mountain.
He thought,
I like my home by the sea.
I do not like the mountains.
In a few days,
they started on the long trip.
It was dark when they came
to Uncle Ralph's house.
In the morning,

Dick went outside.
He looked down–far down
into the valley.
He looked up–far up
to the top of the mountains.
Uncle Ralph came outside, too.
He asked Dick,
"How do you like the mountains?"
"They are so high," said Dick.
"Yes, they are high,"
said Uncle Ralph.
"They make me think of God.
I often talk to God right here."
Dick thought a minute. Then
he smiled and said, "I know
that God is beside the sea.
I forgot that He is here, too.
Now I like the mountains."

A PRESENT FROM GOD

"How can I be sure
that God loves me?" asked Nancy.
Mother smiled at her. She said,
"God sent you a present—
the very best present He had."
"What did He send?" asked Nancy.
"He sent His own Son,
Jesus," answered Mother.
"Did Jesus tell us that God
loved us?" asked Nancy.
"He showed us," said Mother.
"He made sick people well.
He made sad people happy.
He told everyone about God."
"I'm glad He came," said Nancy.
"Most important of all,"
said Mother, "He died for us."
Nancy did not answer. She was
thinking how much God loves us.

HELPING GOD

"Will God take care of me
whatever I do?" asked Barbara.
George said, "God helps you
to take care of yourself."
"God wants us to help Him,"
said Francie.
George said, "If you ride
your tricycle in front of a car,
you might get hurt."
"God will make the car stop
for me," said Barbara.
"Maybe the car will be going
too fast," said George.
Barbara thought a minute.
Then she said, "Last winter
I played outside without my coat,
and I got sick."
As George rode off, he called,
"Take care of yourself."

SAMMY'S WAGON

Father was reading his paper.
"The wheel came off my wagon,"
said Sammy. "Will you fix it?"
"Yes," said Father.
He put down his paper.
They went to the work room.
Father started to fix the wagon.
Sammy thought of Father's paper.
Father liked to read his paper.
Sammy thought, I wish I could
show Father how glad I am
that he is fixing my wagon.
Just then, Father said,
"It is warm in here.
I wish I had a drink of water."
Sammy hurried to the kitchen.
Soon he came back. He said,

"Here is a glass of water
for you, Father."
Father took a big drink.
He said, "I like to help boys
who do nice things for me."

HELPING

Mother did not feel well.

She was lying down.

"I will take care of the house,

Mother," said Terry.

"That will be fine,"

said Mother. "But first, will

you give Joey his bottle?"

"Yes," said Terry.

Joey smiled when he saw

Terry bringing his bottle.

Terry looked around the house.
There were many things to do.
First he took the dishes from
the table to the kitchen sink.
Then he put some birdseed out
for the birds.
Next he played with Joey.
Soon Mother said,
"I am feeling much better now.
Thank you, Terry."
"It is fun to help," said Terry.
"Now I will help someone else.
I will make a house
for the birds in our yard."

MIKE AND RAGS

Ron watched Mike play with his dog.
"Go get the stick, Rags,"
Mike threw a stick in the water.
Rags had to swim hard.
He brought back the stick.
"This is a fast stream,"
said Mike. "Go again!"
So Rags jumped in again,
but the stream was too fast.
It pulled Rags away from Mike.
Rags could not help himself.
Mike did not know what to do.
"I will help you," called Ron.
They held a long stick in the
water for Rags. He caught it.
Ron and Mike pulled Rags out.
"I am sorry, Rags," said Mike.
"I should not have sent you
into the fast stream."

Mary, 2 mos.

MARY'S PICTURE

"May I see my baby picture?"
asked Mary. Mother got it out.
"May I take it outside?"
asked Mary. Mother said,
"No, it might get lost."
But Mary took it outside
and showed it to Diane.
Diane only said,
"Let's go swing on my swing."
Soon it started to rain.
So they played in Diane's house.
Later Mary went home.
Then she thought of something.
She wanted to cry. She said,
"I forgot my picture."
"I know," said Mother.
"I found it and brought it in."
"I am sorry," said Mary.
"I should have listened to you."

GOD IS GOOD

"God is very good," said Jannie.

"Yes," said Lonnie. "He loves us
and takes care of us."

"He made everything,"
said Jannie. "He is everywhere."

"I wish I could tell Him
that I love Him," said Lonnie.

"When you want to tell God
something," said Jannie,
"you pray to Him."

"Can I tell Him anything
I want to?" asked Lonnie.

"Yes," said Jannie. "God wants
you to tell Him everything."

"I am glad," said Lonnie.
"I have many things that I want
to tell God."

"I like to talk to God, too,"
said Jannie.

So Jannie and Lonnie
closed their eyes.
They folded their hands.
Then they talked to God.

FOR BOYS AND GIRLS

"Is the Bible for children?"
asked Karen.
"I do not know," said Randy,
"but I do know that it tells
stories about boys and girls."
"And it tells stories
about animals, too," said Judy.
"Boys and girls like animals."
Karen nodded her head. She said,
"The Bible says, 'God is love.'
And God loves boys and girls."
Randy said, "The Bible tells
a story about children
who came to see Jesus."
Judy added, "Jesus was glad
to see the children."
Karen smiled. She said,
"I am sure now that the Bible
is for children."

Madonna della Sedia

By Raphael Sanzio (1483-1520)
In the Pitti Palace, Florence, Italy
Color Photograph by Alinari Brothers, Florence

THIS is the well-known MADONNA OF THE CHAIR, so-called for the chair (sedia) in which the Madonna is seated. The Madonna lovingly holds the Child Jesus on her knee while little John the Baptist clasps his hands in adoration. The beautiful dark-eyed mother wears on her head the striped handkerchief of Roman women. In her we are given the very essence of human maternal love, universally appealing for her profound humanity. The Children have all the charm of babyhood yet in their expressive, far-seeing eyes we sense the forecast of their divine missions on earth. Added to these beauties is that of rich and glowing color. Little wonder that this is perhaps the best loved of all of Raphael's Madonnas.

This picture is one that appeals alike to the learned and the simple. In this respect THE MADONNA OF THE CHAIR may be compared with another masterpiece by Raphael, Madonna del Gran' Duca (See Vol. 9, page 22.) Both pictures go straight to the common humanity that underlies all the differences of taste, sentiment and education in different people. It is the intense humanity in these two greatest of Raphael's Madonnas that is so wonderful.

The painter, Raphael Sanzio, was born in Urbino, Italy, in 1483. He died in Rome in 1520, at the age of thirty-seven, one year after Leonardo da Vinci and forty-four years before Michelangelo. Raphael's part in this age of giants was to make beauty understandable to all. Through his genius in assimilating the best around him and transforming it into something more perfect, he produced an art which touched the hearts of all men.

Easy
Reading
Bible Stories

JOSEPH GETS A SURPRISE

One day Father said,
"Come here, Joseph."

Joseph went at once to Father.
"I have a surprise for you,"
said Father.
He held up a fine coat.
It was the most beautiful coat
that Joseph had ever seen.
"This new coat is for you,"
said Father.
How pleased Joseph was!
He put on his new coat.
It fit him just right.
Joseph wanted to wear
his new coat all of the time.
"Thank you, Father," he said.

JOSEPH GOES LOOKING

Joseph had ten big brothers
and one little brother.
Sometimes he played games
with his little brother.
Sometimes he helped his big
brothers take care of the sheep.
Sometimes he did things
for Father and helped him.
"Joseph," said Father one day,
"go and find your big brothers.
They have been away watching
the sheep for many days.
See how they are getting along."
So Joseph took a long stick
and his new coat with him.
"Good-by, Father," he called.
Joseph walked and walked.
Then he came to the place where
he thought his brothers were,

but they were not there.

Joseph could not find them.

He did not know where to look.

JOSEPH FINDS HIS BROTHERS

Joseph walked around looking
and looking for his brothers.
A man saw him walking around.
"What are you doing?"
asked the man.
"I am Joseph," he said.
"I am looking for my brothers."
The man said, "They have gone
to another place over there."
"Thank you," said Joseph.

He started off again.
He walked and walked.
At last he came to a place
where he saw many sheep.
His brothers. were there, too.
Joseph was glad to see them
after walking so far.
He was glad that he had done
what his father told him to do.
He had found his brothers.

THE BASKET BOAT

"Our little baby is not safe,"
said Mother. "The wicked king
wants to hurt him."
"We must think of a way
to hide our baby," said Miriam.
They thought and thought.
"We will make a little
basket boat that water
cannot get into," said Mother.
They fixed the basket boat.

Then Mother said, "Now we will
put the baby in the basket boat.
We will put it in the river."
Miriam clapped her hands.
"He will be safe," she said.
"No one will look there for him.
And if he makes any noise,
no one will hear him."
So they put the baby in
the basket boat. They took
the basket boat to the river.
"I will stay here
in the tall grass," said Miriam.
"I will watch the baby."

THE PRINCESS

Miriam watched the basket boat.
Then she saw the princess come
to the river with her maids.
The princess pointed to the
basket boat. "What is that?"
she asked. "Bring it to me."
A maid took the little
basket boat to the princess.
She said, "The baby's mother
must be hiding him from
my father, the king.

He will hurt the baby.
But this is a dear little baby,
so I will keep him safe."

A NURSE FOR THE BABY

Miriam ran to the princess.

"I know a good nurse," she said,

"to take care of the baby."

The princess smiled. She said,

"Bring the nurse to me."

So Miriam ran home.

She said to Mother,

"The princess found our baby.

She wants you to be his nurse."

They hurried back together.

The princess said, "I found
this baby in the river.
I will name him Moses.
Take him to your home. I will
pay you to take care of him."
They took their baby home.
Mother and Miriam
were not afraid now.
Their baby was safe because
the princess loved him.

THE SHEPHERD BOY

David was a shepherd boy.

He watched his Father's sheep.

He took the sheep
up into the hills.
He found green grass for
the sheep to eat.
He found clear streams of water
for the sheep to drink.
The little lambs needed
grass and water to grow strong.
Sometimes a little lamb
got tired of walking.
Then, David carried it in his
arms for a while.
When the sun was hot, he found
a shady place for the sheep.
When night came, he found
a place for them to sleep.
David loved his sheep.
He asked God to help him,
and God helped him to take
good care of his sheep.

THE BOY AND THE LION

One night the sheep were asleep,
but David was watching.
All at once he saw a shadow.
He saw the shadow move.
It was not the shadow of a tree.
It was not the shadow of a sheep.
It was the shadow of a lion.
The lion was walking quietly
toward a little lamb.
The little lamb was sleeping.
David ran to the lamb.
He held it under his arm.
He reached quickly for a stone.
The lion was very near.
David threw the stone.
The lion seemed to know
that David was not afraid.
The lion turned and ran away.
The little lamb was afraid.

But David held it close to him.

Then, it was not afraid.

The lamb went back to sleep.

THE BOY AND HIS HARP

David liked to be out
in the hills with his sheep.
He could watch the sunset
and the sunrise.
He could see the flowers and
the trees and the hills.
He knew that God had made them.
He felt very close to God.
Sometimes the sheep
heard a strange noise.
Then, they were afraid.

So David would talk to them.
The sheep knew his voice.
Then, they were not afraid.
David had a little harp
on which he played music.
He made up poems about God
and about the things he saw.
He made up music
to go with the poems.
While he watched his sheep,
David played on his harp.
He sang his songs to tell God
that he loved Him.

ELISHA TELLS ABOUT GOD

Elisha walked from town to town.
He told people about God.
When Elisha came into a town,
the boys and girls
hurried to meet him.
The men and women were glad
to see Elisha, too.

They liked to hear him
tell about God.
And Elisha liked
to tell people about God.
But, he got very tired
walking from town to town.
He often said to himself,
"I wish I had a home of my own.
I wish I had a place to stay
when I get tired."
But, Elisha had no home.

A WOMAN HELPS ELISHA

A rich man and his kind wife
lived in the town of Shunem.
They heard how Elisha
walked from town to town.
The kind woman said to Elisha,
"Come into my house and rest.
Let me give you food and water."
So Elisha went in and rested.

He had a fine dinner.

After that, the woman often

gave Elisha his dinner.

The woman said to her husband,

"Elisha is a good man.

He does not have a home.

I would like to build a room

for him where he could rest."

Her husband asked,

"Where would we build the room?"

His wife answered,

"Right on our flat roof."

"Yes, let us do that,"

said her husband.

ELISHA GETS A HOME

The kind woman hired
some workmen. She told them,
"Please build a room
on our flat roof."
First the workmen built
a stairway beside the house.
Then, they built the room.
"Now," said the woman, "I will
get the room ready for Elisha.
I will put in a bed, a chair,
a table, and a lamp."

One day Elisha came back to Shunem.

The woman hurried to meet him.

"Elisha," she said, "I have

something to show you."

The woman and her husband

led Elisha up the stairway.

They took him into the room.

"This is your room,"

said the woman.

"This is your new home."

Elisha was surprised.

He was very happy! At last

he had a home of his very own!

THE LITTLE DONKEY

Clip, clop, clip, clop went
the little donkey's small feet.
Mary rode on the little donkey.
Joseph walked beside them.
They were going to Bethlehem.
The king told them to go there.
Each man had to go to the town

where his grandfather had lived.
They had to go to be counted.
So Joseph had to go to Bethlehem
to be counted.
They walked for many miles.
At last they came to Bethlehem.
It was night. They were tired.
Joseph went to an inn.
He knocked on the door.
The innkeeper came to the door.
Mary waited for Joseph,
on the little donkey.

THE STABLE

"Can Mary and I stay
in your inn?" asked Joseph.
The innkeeper said, "I am sorry.
The inn is full tonight.
Many people have come
to Bethlehem to be counted.
Many people are staying here."
Then the innkeeper said, "But
I have a stable behind the inn.
You may stay there if you like.
Come, I will show you."
They went out into the night
together. He held his light high
so that Joseph could see.
They went to a stable.
The stable was a small room
where animals were kept.
There was hay on the floor.
The mangers were filled with

grass for the animals to eat.
"Thank you," said Joseph
to the innkeeper.
Then Joseph led Mary, on the
little donkey, into the stable.
Joseph made a fine bed of hay
for Mary.
He put his coat around her
to keep her warm.
Mary was glad to rest in the
stable after the long trip.

THE BABY

The stars shone brightly.
In the stable a
little baby was born
to Mary and Joseph.
It was a beautiful baby!
Mary dressed the little Baby
in soft, warm clothes.
Joseph put sweet-smelling

grass in a manger.

He put the manger beside
Mary's bed of hay.

They laid the little Baby
in the manger.

Joseph looked at the Baby.
He asked,

"What shall we call Him?"

Mary answered,

"His name is Jesus."

THE SHEPHERDS

Over the hill from
the little town of Bethlehem,
shepherds watched their sheep.
The sheep were sleeping.
The shepherds sat near a fire
to keep warm in the cool night.

They talked in quiet voices.
One shepherd said,
"God has said He would send
Someone to help us.
When will He come?"
Another answered,
"We have waited many years
for God to send Someone."
One of them said,
"I hope that God will send
Someone to help us
before I grow old and die."
All at once, a great light
was all around the shepherds.
They looked up in surprise.
A shining angel stood
in the great light!
The shepherds covered
their faces with their coats.
They were afraid.

SHEPHERDS HEAR THE ANGEL

The angel told the shepherds,

"Do not be afraid.

I bring you good news.

It will make everyone happy.

God sent Someone to help you.

He was born this very night.

He was born in Bethlehem.

He will be your Savior.

You will find this little
Baby lying in a manger."
Then many other angels
appeared. They sang,
"Glory to God in Heaven,
and on earth, peace among men."

SHEPHERDS FIND THE BABY

All at once the angels were gone.

It was dark again.

The shepherds talked about

this wonderful news. They said,

"We must go to Bethlehem now."

One of the shepherds

said to the others,

"You go to Bethlehem.

I will stay here with the sheep.

Hurry back to tell me about it."

So the shepherds

went to Bethlehem.

They found the stable where

Mary and Joseph were staying.

Joseph came to the door.

"God told us about

the new Baby," they said.

"We have come to see Him."

The shepherds went in quietly.

And there was the little Baby.
He was lying in a manger—
just as the angel had told them.
He was such a fine little Baby!
The shepherds thought,
God has sent Him to help us.
They felt very close to God
as they looked at the Baby.
Then, they went away.
They told many people
about the new Baby.
And they thanked God
for sending the Baby.

THE WISE MEN

"See that bright star,"
said a man who was very wise.
"Maybe it is telling us
about a new King sent by God."
"Let us find out,"
said another Wise Man.
They got on their camels
and rode for many days.
Then, they came to a big city.
They went to see the old king.
They said, "We saw the star
of the new king.
We have come to Him."
The king told them,
"Go to Bethlehem
and find this new King.
Then tell me where He is.
I want to see Him, too."

The Wise Men rode on their
camels out of the big city.
When night came, they looked up
and saw the bright star.
They followed it to Bethlehem.

FOLLOWING THE STAR

The Wise Men rode
on their camels into Bethlehem.
They watched the star.
It stopped above a little house.
Jesus and Mary and Joseph
lived in the little house, now.
The Wise Men told Joseph,
"We saw the star of the Baby.
We have come to see Him."

Quietly, the Wise Men
went into the little house.
The Wise Men kneeled down
on the floor in front of Jesus.
They bowed their heads.
They prayed, "Thank You, God,
for helping us find Jesus."
Then, they opened some boxes.
They had brought fine presents
with them on their camels.
They gave these fine presents
to Jesus because they loved Him.

THE DREAM

The Wise Men smiled at Jesus.
They loved Him so much!
Then they went home.
Little Jesus was soon asleep.
Mary and Joseph went to sleep.
Then Joseph had a dream.
In his dream, God sent an angel.
The angel said, "Get up, Joseph.
Take Mary and the little Child
to another country.

The wicked king of this
country wants to hurt Jesus."
So Joseph and Mary got up
while it was still dark.
They started at once.
They had to go a long, long way
to get to the other country.
When they got there Joseph said,
"Now little Jesus is safe. Here
he will grow tall and strong.
God took good care of us."

A SICK BOY

A boy was very sick.
His mother and father
were afraid that their son
would not get well.
So, the father went to see Jesus.
He had to walk to another town.
The father said to Jesus,
"My son is very sick.
Please come and make him well."
Jesus said, "Go back home.
Your son is well now."
And, sure enough,
at that very minute,
the boy got well.
The mother and father were
happy that their son was well.
The boy was happy too.
They were so happy that they
all wanted to be Jesus' helpers.

JESUS GETS NEW HELPERS

Jesus sat in Peter's boat.

He talked to many people.

Then, the people went away.

Jesus said to Peter,

"Take your boat into deep water.

Then go fishing there."

Peter said,

"We fished all night.

We did not catch any fish,

but we will do as you say."

So, they rowed out into the lake.

And they caught many fish!

Peter's friends in another boat

had to help pull in the fish.

Jesus said to Peter and

his friends, "Come with me.

Be my helpers."

So, they went with Jesus

to be his helpers.

THE LITTLE LOST LAMB

Jesus told a story about
a shepherd who had 100 sheep.
He counted his sheep every night.
One night he counted
1, 2, 3 — up to 99.
One was missing.
At once the shepherd
went to look for the lost sheep.
He walked up the hills.
He walked through the fields.
He looked near the streams.
He looked behind big rocks.
Then he heard, "Baa — baa."
The poor little lamb
was caught in the bushes.
The shepherd took the little
lamb in his arms.
How happy the lamb was that
his shepherd loved him so much.

JESUS AND THE BOYS AND GIRLS

Jesus was very busy.

He was talking to many people.

Some boys and girls wanted

to see Jesus and talk to Him.

But Jesus' helpers said,

"No, He is too busy to talk to you."

How sad the boys and girls felt!

They turned to go away.

But, Jesus had heard His helpers.

Jesus said,

"Do not send the children away.

They are my friends."

Jesus took the little children

on his lap.

The bigger boys and girls

stood close to Him.

"Jesus is our Friend,"

said the boys and girls.

"He loves us."

JESUS LOVES HIS FRIENDS

Jesus went to a garden to pray.
Jesus prayed, "Father, I will do
what you want me to do."
Jesus knew that people wanted
to hurt Him and His friends,
but Jesus was not afraid.
Jesus knew that they wanted
to kill Him and His friends.
Jesus loved His friends so much!
He was glad to die for them.
He died for all of His friends.
How sad Jesus' friends felt!
They buried Jesus in a cave.
Then one morning, some of
Jesus' friends went to the cave.
But Jesus was not there!
Jesus was alive again!
And Jesus still lives today.

Children's
Prayers

TABLE PRAYERS

THANK YOU GOD

Thank You, God,
For milk and bread
    And other things so good;
Thank You, God,
For those who help
    To grow and cook our food.

—Elizabeth M. Schields

FOR ALL OUR FOOD

For fruit and milk,
For bread and meat,
For all our food so good to eat,
We thank You, God.

GOD IS GREAT

God is great
    And God is good;
Let us thank Him
    For our food.

FOR FOOD SO GOOD

Thank You, God,
    For food so good;
And help us do
    The things we should.

COME LORD JESUS

Come Lord Jesus
    Be our guest;
May our food
    By Thee be blessed.

MORNING PRAYERS

THE GLAD MORNING LIGHT

Thank You, dear God,
　　For sleep through the night;
Thank You, dear God,
　　For the glad morning light.

THIS HAPPY DAY

I thank You, God,
　　For sleep last night,
I thank You for the
　　Morning light;
I thank You for
　　This happy day,
Please help me keep it
　　Just that way.

A HAPPY SONG

Early in the morning
　　I sing a happy song:
"God will be my helper,
　　All this whole day long!"

NIGHT TIME PRAYERS

THANK YOU FOR MY DAY

Now the sun has gone to sleep,
    And birds are in their nest;
So I will thank You for my day—
My busy day of work and play—
    And then I'll go to rest.

DEAR GOD

Dear God, I've had a happy day,
    I tried to do my best.
And now I thank You for the night
    When children all can rest.

MY EVENING PRAYER

Dear God, hear my evening prayer:
I thank You for Your love and care,
I thank You for this happy day,
For home and friends, for work and play—
Bless the ones I love tonight,
And keep us all 'til morning light.

THANK YOU FOR THE NIGHT

Thank You, God, for the night—
    For the shining stars
    And the quiet dark,
    For my own little bed
    And for rest and sleep.
Thank You, God, for the night.

ASKING PRAYERS

FORGIVE ME GOD

Forgive me, God, for things I do
That are not kind and good.
Forgive me, God, and help me try
To do the things I should.

TODAY I FORGOT

Today I forgot to be kind, dear God,
And friendly to everyone;
Please help me to remember,
And then we'll all have fun.

—Elizabeth M. Schields

HELP ME THINK

Dear God, I said
Some cross words
And quarreled some today,
Please help me think
Of kind words
And pleasant ways to play.

—Elizabeth M. Schields

LIKE HIM TO BE

Dear God,
I like to think
Of Jesus who was a child
Like me.
Help me
In all my work and play
To try my best in every way,
And so, like Him to be.

—Elizabeth M. Schields

THANK YOU PRAYERS

THANK YOU FOR LOVING ME

Thank You, dear God, for loving me
    When I do the things I should;
Thank You, God, for loving me
    Even when I am not good.
Thank You, God for loving me.

THE GOOD WORLD

Thank You, dear God,
For the good world You have planned:
For rain and wind and snowflakes;
For trees and grass and flowers;
For birds and pets and horses;
For books and music and pictures;
For home and school and church.
Thank You, dear God,
For the good world You have planned.

GOD OUR FATHER

For lovely things
    I hear and see,
And happy thoughts
    That come to me;
Thank You, God, our Father.

—*Elizabeth M. Schields*

HELP ME TO SHARE

I thank You for my picture books,
    I thank You for my toys;
Please help me, God, to share them
    With other girls and boys.

MY
BIBLE
READER

Holy Family

By Carlo Maratta (1625-1713)
In the Vatican Gallery, Rome
Color Photograph by Alinari Brothers, Florence

IN this painting Mary's face, very tender and beautiful, is of the Italian type. Joseph, with a fine, serious expression, is offering strawberries to the infant Jesus who has already taken one. The Holy Family appears to be partaking of a meal. Mary holds a saucer in her hand; a basket and jar are on the ground at the left. Above Mary's head an angel holds a wreath-shaped bouquet. Behind, two children, perhaps angels, are singing from a book. How do we know that the Holy Family is in Egypt?

The artist, Carlo Maratta, was born in Camerano, Italy in 1625 and died in Rome in 1713. He early showed artistic talent and at eleven, as was then the custom, started his studies with Andrea Sacchi (1599-1661), a leading art teacher in Rome. After 1650 he became one of the most popular painters there. He was employed by several successive Popes; was appointed superintendent of paintings in the Vatican, and finally was entrusted with the exacting task of cleaning and restoring the priceless frescoes by Raphael in the Vatican. Maratta belonged to the late seventeenth century Roman school and was influenced by the two main tendencies in painting of this period, which were, eclecticism or a return to the principles of the great masters, and naturalism or a conscientious, realistic representation of outward appearances. Maratta was the last great draughtsman of his time. In Italian art he ranks as a minor artist, as do most Italian painters after the sixteenth century.

A comparison of this picture with those by Raphael (see page 74) and Luini (Vol. 2:180) shows that Maratta was a pleasing, talented artist if not very profound or original. Paintings by other seventeenth century artists are on page 22 and Vol. 2:42, 194, 274.

The World Around Us

Pete's Happy Birthday

Pete stood on his side of the fence. "Hi, Larry," he called to his friend, who lived next door. "Come and see my new birthday presents."

So, Larry climbed over the fence into Pete's yard. His dog, King, crawled underneath.

"What did you get?" asked Larry.

"Come around back and see," he said. "Aunt Jane sent me this tether ball."

He pointed to a tall pole. It had a ball fastened to it with a long rope.

"And see the ping pong set I got from Grand-

146

mother," he added. "Dad fixed this table so we can play ping pong in the yard."

"It looks like fun," said Larry. "Let's play."

"I'll start," Pete said. He picked up a ping pong paddle. The boys played three games. King ran back and forth between the two boys trying to keep up with the ball. He soon got tired and lay down under the table.

"Why can't I be first sometimes?" asked Larry.

"Because it's my ping pong set," Pete said.

Larry put down his paddle. "I'm tired of this. Let's do something else."

Pete caught the tether ball and hit it. "Watch out.

147

Here it comes," he said.

"It's my turn to be first," said Larry. "You started all of the other games."

"Well, it's my tether ball. If you don't like it, you can just go home." Pete said.

"All right, Mr. Selfish," said Larry. "I will go home, and I'm not coming back ever."

"Be sure to stay there," Pete called.

Larry took the long way home through Pete's front yard. He walked through the gate. King followed him.

Pete kicked at a rock. He picked up a ping pong paddle. He batted the ball. He couldn't play ping pong by himself.

Pete walked over to the tether ball. He was angry. He hit it hard and watched it wind around the pole. But it wasn't fun playing tether ball by himself.

"What a birthday," said Pete to himself. "I started this fight by being selfish. And now I don't have anyone to play with."

Larry was in the back yard on the other side of the fence. He got his baseball. He threw it into the air. It wasn't any fun when Pete wasn't there to catch.

"I wish I hadn't fought with Pete," he said to himself. "His toys are new. I should have let him be first."

Larry walked over to the fence. He wanted to see

148

what Pete was doing. Did Pete really mean what he said? thought Larry. Did he want me to stay home for good?

Pete looked around his yard. It looked so lonely when he had to play all by himself. Did Larry really mean what he said? thought Pete. Will he and King never come to play again?

Pete walked over to the fence. He wanted to see what Larry was doing. And there was Larry, looking over the fence into Pete's yard. Pete looked at Larry, and Larry looked at Pete.

Then both boys began to laugh.

"It's no fun playing by myself," said Pete.

"I don't like it either," said Larry.

"I'm sorry that I was selfish with my birthday toys," said Pete. "Please come back. You can be first this time."

"Oh that's all right," said Larry, and he climbed over the fence again.

149

Tag-Along-Tim

Jan ran up the front steps two at a time. Taffy ran up behind her. "Mother!" called Jan. "Come quick. Tim's hurt."

Mother came running out to Tim.

"I cut my arm," cried Tim. "It's bleeding." He started to cry loudly. Taffy started to bark.

"It's not too bad," said Mother. "We'll have it fixed in a minute. Quiet, Taffy."

Mother washed Tim's cut. Tim cried even louder. "Ow! Ow! It hurts."

"Tim tags along everywhere I go," said Jan. "He always spoils my fun. When I took him to Linda's picnic, he got lost. We spent the whole time looking for him. We didn't even get to swim."

Mother wrapped a cloth around Tim's arm. He stopped crying.

"The other day he followed me to Carol's," Jan went on. "He ran with my doll and broke her. So we didn't get to play dolls at all."

"And what happened today?" asked Mother.

"This time he had to tag along to the park," said Jan. "He was showing off on the swings. He fell and cut his arm."

151

Mother put her arm around Jan. "Little brothers are sometimes hard to get along with. But God wants us to be forgiving."

"But how many times do I have to forgive him?" asked Jan. "He is always doing something. I just can't forgive him any more."

"Do you ever do things that make God sad?" asked Mother.

"Yes," said Jan slowly.

"Does God ever forgive you?" Mother asked.

"Lots of times," said Jan. She thought a bit. "Lots more times than I have ever forgiven Tim."

"I'm really sorry, Jan. Honest," said Tim.

Jan smiled, "Oh, all right then. I forgive you."

"I see that the blackberries are ripe," said Mother. "If you walk down the road and pick some, I will bake a pie. You will have to hurry, Father will be home soon."

"Yum. I like blackberry pie," said Jan. "And I'll show you I really forgive you, Tim. I will take you with me." She picked up two shiny tin pails.

Jan and Tim and Taffy walked down the road. They walked a long way to the blackberry patch.

"Did you ever see so many berries?" asked Jan. *Plink. Plunk.* The berries bounced into the pails as Jan and Tim picked them.

They went farther into the blackberry patch. Jan climbed up on a big log. She reached up over the top

152

of a big blackberry bush. *Plunk,* went the big berries into her pail.

She jumped down. Her foot slipped into a hole and she fell. "Oh! Ouch!" she said. "Oh, Tim, I hurt my foot. It hurts."

Tim and Taffy hurried to Jan.

"I can't walk on it," said Jan. "You must go get Father."

"All by myself?" asked Tim.

"Take Taffy with you," she said.

"No," said Tim, standing up very straight. "I'll go by myself. Taffy, you stay with Jan."

Tim ran through the blackberry patch.

Taffy sat down beside Jan. They waited for what seemed like a long time. Finally, Tim came back with Father. Jan was so glad to see them! Father carried Jan home.

Later Jan hugged Tim. "I'm glad you were with me," she said. "I might have been there for hours. I will never call you Tag-Along-Tim again."

The Grumble Family

"Dinner is almost ready, Linda," Mother said. "Please call Father and Dan now."

"But they are somewhere outside, Mom. It will take me all day to find them," Linda grumbled.

"Dinner will be cold by then," said Mother. "Now hurry."

At last everyone was at the table. They bowed their heads. Father thanked God for the food. He asked God to help their family live to please Jesus.

When Father was through praying, Dan said, "Why did Linda have to call me right in the middle of our Monday night ball game?"

"Dinner was ready too soon for me, too," said Father. "I wasn't through fixing the car."

"You should be glad you didn't have to come in and set the table," grumbled Linda.

"Or cook the dinner on such a hot day," Mother said.

Everyone at the table looked very cross.

Then Father said, "We just asked God to help us please Him. But we have each grumbled about something."

"The Bible says we should find happiness in the Lord all of the time," Mother said. "But we are just a Grumble Family."

"We are so used to grumbling," said Linda. "It would be hard to stop."

"Let's do something to help us remember," said Father.

"But what?" asked Dan.

"We could play a Grumble Game," said Mother. "Please get those funny toy glasses you got at Johnny's birthday party, Dan."

When Dan came back, Mother put the four pairs of toy glasses in a box. "When anyone grumbles at dinner, he has to wear a pair of these Grumble Glasses," said Mother.

"How long do we have to wear them?" Linda asked.

"We can take them off when we help with the dinner dishes," said Mother.

"But I hate to do dishes," grumbled Dan.

"Give Dan the first pair of Grumble Glasses," said Father. So Dan had to put on the funny glasses.

"No one is going to catch me," said Linda.

"We hope not," Mother said. She passed Linda a big bowl. "Have you had any carrots yet, Linda?"

"No, and I don't want any. I don't like carrots," Linda grumbled.

"Linda gets Grumble Glasses, too," Dan laughed.

When dinner was over, everyone had on Grumble Glasses. "There are plenty of helpers to do dishes tonight," said Father.

"Maybe we will do better tomorrow," Mother said.

And on Tuesday night, Mother remembered not to grumble. On Wednesday, Father remembered, too. On Thursday night, Dan did not grumble, and Linda had to do the dishes all by herself. On Friday night no one had to wear Grumble Glasses.

"Even carrots taste better when we are all cheerful," said Linda.

"There is no one to do the dishes tonight," Dan said.

"When we are cheerful helpers, it pleases Jesus. It makes our family happy, too," said Linda. "I'll help with the dishes."

"Me, too," said Dan. "And we won't need the Grumble Glasses any more."

Friends for Ken

"Here comes Joe," said Ricky. "Now our Tree House Club can have a meeting."

"Come on up Joe," called Paul.

Joe climbed up the ladder to the Tree House.

"It's fun to have our own Tree House," said Paul.

The boys heard a big truck coming. It stopped at the empty house across the street.

"Someone is moving in," said Ricky. "This is a good place to watch from."

"Maybe we can tell if there are any boys in the family," said Joe.

They watched as the moving men took out the family's furniture.

"They must have a baby," said Paul. "They have a crib and a high chair."

"Everything is pink, so it must be a girl," said Joe, who had three sisters. "I wonder if they have any boys."

"There's a boy's bicycle," said Ricky. "They must have a boy big enough to play with us."

The moving truck was soon empty. It drove away. A car came up the street and stopped. The new family got out.

"What did I tell you?" Joe said. "The baby is a girl."

"And there is the boy. Look how short he is. And his name should be Big Ears," Paul said. The boys laughed.

"I don't like his looks," said Joe. "He is not going to play in our Tree House."

They watched the new boy as he stood in his yard. The boy looked all around as if looking for someone to play with. He did not look happy.

"I am going over to meet the new boy," said Ricky.

"If you play with him, you can't play with us," said Joe.

"I don't care," said Ricky. "Father says it pleases God when we are friendly to all our neighbors."

Ricky climbed down the ladder and ran across the street. "Hello," he said. "I am Ricky Johnson. What's your name?"

"I am Ken Jones." The new boy smiled.

"Could you come to my house to play?" asked Ricky.

"Mother wants me to stay at home today. But if Dad can find my racing car, we could have fun rolling down this hill," said Ken.

Mr. Jones found the car. It was fun taking turns. Ken and Ricky laughed happily.

The boys across the street stayed in the Tree House.

"I wish we had been friendly to the new boy," said Paul. "Ricky is having more fun than we are."

They watched Ken and Ricky go into the garage.

160

"Come see my pets," said Ken. "We have to keep them in here until Dad can build a pen for them."

Each carried a white rabbit into the front yard.

The boys in the Tree House watched Ricky and Ken with the rabbits.

"That Ricky has all the luck," said Joe.

"It is our own fault," said Paul. "He was friendly to the new boy. We were not."

Ricky looked up into the Tree House. "Come on over and see the rabbits," Ricky called.

Ken looked up, too. "You can hold this one," he called.

"The new boy is kinder than we were," Paul said. "He will be a good one to belong to our Tree House club after all," Paul climbed down the rope ladder.

Joe was right behind him.

Keith Gets Angry

Keith stood with his nose pressed against the window and looked out. Then he turned around and said in a loud voice, "It's not going to rain. I want to go outside."

"I told you 'No,' Keith," said Mother. "You have a cold and it's starting to rain right now."

"Please!" begged Keith. "Please!"

"No, you may not go out!" said Mother.

Keith frowned. "But I want to go out," he said angrily.

"I'm going down to the basement," said Mother,

162

"and when I come back I'd like to see a smiling boy instead of a frowning boy."

"I'll show her," muttered Keith, after Mother had left the room.

He kicked the chair nearest him three times. Then he kicked all the other chairs, muttering, "I want to go out. I want to go out. I want to go out!"

He stuck out his lower lip and kicked a little table. The table toppled over and a vase of flowers hit the floor with a loud crash.

"Ouch!" said Keith. He caught his foot between his hands and hopped around on the other foot. "That old table hurt my foot. Mean old table!"

But Keith didn't watch where he was hopping. He hopped where water had spilled out of the vase onto the floor.

Keith's foot slipped from under him and his head banged against the floor.

"Now my head hurts, too," said Keith getting up. He felt like crying. "Mean old water!"

Keith picked up the vase. "Mean old vase," he said. He banged the vase against the wall and it broke into many pieces. One little piece bounced off the wall and hit him on the cheek.

"Ouch!" said Keith. He put his hand on his cheek and felt something wet.

"I'm cut!" shouted Keith. "I'm bleeding."

Just then Mother came into the room. She looked around and said. "Oh, Keith, what have you been doing?" Then she saw his cut. She shook her head. "Well, come and I'll put a bandage on your cut."

While Mother washed Keith's face and put on a bandage, Keith told her about hurting his foot and hitting his head on the floor.

He was beginning to feel better now. He helped Mother wipe up the water and put the flowers in another vase.

"Keith," said Mother quietly, "let's play a game— a special game."

"All right," said Keith eagerly.

"We'll pretend that Jesus is visiting us," said

164

Mother. "When we want to shout or kick or get angry, we'll pretend that Jesus is sitting right there in that chair."

Mother pointed to a chair that Keith had kicked.

"If Jesus was sitting there," said Keith, "I wouldn't have kicked that chair at all."

He looked around the room. How strange it would be if Jesus came to visit them!

"If Jesus came to visit me when I was angry," said Keith, "He would go away again."

"Yes, I think He would," said Mother.

That night when he went to bed, Keith said, "Next time I get angry, I'll remember to play that game."

Steven Gets Even

"Here I come," called Steven. He slid down the slide. Just as he reached the bottom, Tuffy stuck out his foot and tripped him. Steven stumbled and fell. Tuffy laughed and walked away.

Steven stood up and rubbed his knee. "I'll get even with him," he said angrily.

The next day it rained. There were puddles of water everywhere. Just as Steven came into the schoolyard, Tuffy bumped against him. Steven's reading book fell in a big puddle. As Steven bent over to pick it up, Tuffy pushed him.

Splash! Steven had fallen into the puddle. Tuffy laughed and ran off around the schoolhouse.

"You just wait, Tuffy!" Steven called after him. "I'll get even with you!"

Steven stood up. Elaine and Joy came into the schoolyard. Elaine picked up his lunch box for him and Joy picked up his book.

"That Tuffy is mean to everybody," said Elaine, shaking the water off the lunch box.

"I wish I could get even," said Steven angrily.

"But, if you do something mean to him," said Joy, "then he will do something mean to you."

"Well, then how would you get even with him?" asked Steven crossly.

"You know what our Sunday school teacher told us," said Joy. "The best way to get along with mean people is to be kind to them."

"I remember that story," said Elaine. "Some people were not kind to Jesus. But Jesus said, 'Do good to them that hate you.' "

"It really works, too," Joy said. "Why not try it on Tuffy?"

"Well . . . all right," Steven said. "I don't know if I can think of anything kind to do. But I'll try."

As they were going into their classroom, Steven saw Tuffy coming down the hall. "Hi, Tuffy," he said kindly.

"Get out of my way," said Tuffy. He pushed Steven against the wall.

Steven felt like doing something mean to Tuffy! "But I said I would get even God's way," Steven told himself.

Later that day, the teacher said, "We need someone to build some boxes. We must have them for our science class next week."

Steven raised his hand, "I think Tuffy would be best for the job. He made a good soap box racer all by himself. He knows more about making things than any boy in our class."

The boys and girls looked surprised. No one had

ever said anything nice about Tuffy. But what Steven had said was really true.

Tuffy looked more surprised than anyone else. He even smiled when he said he would make the boxes.

At lunch time Tuffy sat down by Steven. "How about helping me with those boxes, Steve?" he asked. "We could do it at my house after school."

"Thanks, that would be fun," said Steven. Tuffy grinned. "I thought you were going to get even with me," he said.

"I did get even," said Steven, smiling. "I got even God's way."

Tuffy thought a minute. Then he said, "I think I'll try that way, too."

The Grocery Store Window

"Catch!" said Greg, tossing the ball to Harry.

Harry caught the ball and tossed it back. "Be careful of the store windows," he said. "I broke two last year. Now everybody thinks I break windows all the time."

"Okay," said Greg. He tossed the ball again. Harry grabbed for it, but missed.

"You should have caught it," said Greg.

Harry ran after the ball and tossed it to Greg. "I have to go home, now," he said.

Greg looked around for someone else to play catch with. He saw Bud across the street, coming out of the grocery store.

I'll play a joke on Bud, he thought, I'll throw the ball, then hide behind a tree. He won't know who threw it.

So Greg stood beside a tree and threw the ball. "Here, catch!" he shouted. Then he jumped behind the tree.

Crash! Greg heard the sound of a window breaking. Carefully he peeked out from behind the tree. The grocery store window was broken.

"It's your fault," he shouted at Bud, running across the street. "You should have caught the ball."

"Who threw that ball?" said Mr. Barker, coming

out of his grocery store. He was carrying the ball.

"I'm sorry," said Bud. "I should have caught the ball and I didn't. He threw it."

"No I didn't," said Greg. "Harry did. He's always breaking windows. He ran home."

"I see," said Mr. Barker. "Well, I'll just keep the ball." He turned and went into the store.

"I thought you threw the ball," said Bud. "Didn't you call to me to catch it?"

"Not me," said Greg. "I told you—Harry threw it."

"Well, I have to go home," said Bud.

Bud hurried off. But he turned and looked at Greg for a minute just before he went around the corner.

"I hope nobody saw me," said Greg to himself, as he hurried home.

That night before he went to bed Greg thought about saying his prayers. But somehow he didn't feel like praying.

In the morning, Greg went the long way around to school. He did not want to pass Harry's house. And he did not want to pass the grocery store, either.

Once his teacher called on him to recite and he didn't even hear her. "What's wrong?" she asked. "Are you sleepy today?"

Greg just shook his head.

After school Greg walked slowly down the street. He turned the corner and walked along the sidewalk toward the grocery store. He walked slower and slower. Finally he came to the grocery store. Slowly he opened the door and went in.

"Mr. Barker," he said in a quiet voice, "I'm sorry. I told a lie. I threw the ball."

Mr. Barker put his hand on Greg's shoulder. "I know," he said. "I saw you."

Greg looked up at Mr. Barker. "You saw me!" he said. "But you didn't say so."

"No," said Mr. Barker. "I wanted you to tell the truth."

Greg could not look at Mr. Barker. Greg looked down at his shoes. "I am sorry I lied. I feel better now that I have told you the truth."

Then Greg looked at the window. It was still broken. "I don't have very much money," he said sadly. "I don't know if I can pay for the window."

"It just happens," said Mr. Barker, "that I have a job for a boy who's brave enough to tell the truth."

All Around the World

"When Jesus lived on earth, He didn't live in our country, did He?" asked Susie.

"No," said Charlie. "He lived in a land far across the ocean."

Susie frowned. She asked, "If Jesus lived so far from here, how did we get to know about him?"

"Some of Jesus' helpers went to other countries and told the people there about Jesus," explained Ronnie. "These people, in turn, went to still other countries."

"And finally, people who loved Jesus came to our country," said Susie.

"There must be boys and girls all around the world who love Jesus just like we do," said Charlie. "I would like to know some of them."

"In Sunday school, we pray for boys and girls in other countries," said Ronnie.

"They are Jesus' friends, just like we are Jesus' friends," said Susie.

"If they are Jesus' friends, and we are Jesus' friends," said Charlie, "then we are all friends."

"Yes," said Susie. "That means that we have friends all around the world."

My Church

"I don't think I'll go to church today," Jeff told his family.

Mother looked at Jeff. Then she asked, "Do you know that some people *can't* go to church today?"

"Why?" asked Jeff.

Jeff's sister, Louise, nodded her head. "Some people are sick in bed, so they have to stay home."

"And some people," said Mother, "don't have a church to go to."

"I wish I didn't have a church to go to," said Jeff. "Then I'd never have to go."

"You mean they have no church at all?" asked Louise in surprise.

Just then the baby cried and Mother went into the baby's room.

"If some people don't even have a church, why do we need one?" asked Jeff.

Louise thought a minute. "Well," she said, "in church they tell us things we should do. And things we shouldn't do. We learn about God and about the Bible, too."

"And we hear stories about Jesus," said Jeff. "I like to hear about Jesus. He's my best Friend."

Mother came in with the baby. Mother had her hat on, ready for church.

"I've been thinking," said Jeff to Mother. "If we didn't have any church, we wouldn't learn about Jesus."

"I'm glad we have a church to go to," said Louise.

"So am I," said Jeff. "I wouldn't miss going to my church for anything."

Julita's Bible

Julita ran up the jungle path to her house near the Amazon River. "Maria," she called to her older sister. "Is it time to go to the river for the Bible meeting?"

Maria was crying. "What's wrong?" asked Julita. "Why aren't you ready to go?"

"I'm not going," said Maria.

"But you have to," said Julita. "We have been waiting so long for this day. We have learned twenty-five verses from God's Book. If you say them all, the Bible-man will give you a Bible all your very own."

"I want to go," said Maria. "But Mother is sick. One of us must stay at home."

"Let me stay with Mother," said Julita.

"Thank you, Little Sister, but Mother needs me." Then Maria smiled. "God knows what is best. You must go for me."

"But I have not even tried to learn all the verses," said Julita. "Carlos and Rosa and Marco are big like you. They have worked hard. But I don't know enough verses."

"You have helped me learn mine," said Maria. "It would not hurt to try. Take Pedro and go. Hurry or you will be late."

179

"Ask God to help me, Maria," Julita said.

"I will," said Maria. "Now go with God."

Pedro and Julita ran down the jungle path. A parrot flew over their heads. A monkey chattered behind them and dropped a banana peel.

"Do you think you know enough verses to get a Bible?" asked Pedro.

"No," Julita said sadly. "I wish I did. We do not have a Bible at home. I want one more than anything."

"Look! There's the Bible-man's boat," Pedro said, pointing to the boat tied up at the river's edge. "Let's run."

Soon the children came to the meeting place beside the wide river. They told the missionary about Maria.

"That is too bad," he said. "She might have won a Bible."

"I will try for her," said Julita bravely.

After the meeting, the missionary stood up. He said, "I wish I had enough Bibles for everyone. But I can only give Bibles to the boys and girls who have learned twenty-five verses."

One by one, the boys and girls said their verses. Marco said twenty-five. He was so proud! Rosa said twenty-five verses, too.

But Carlos could only remember fifteen. He felt so sad!

Then it was Julita's turn. She looked at the faces

before her. She was afraid. Maria is praying for me, she thought. I will pretend that Maria is saying the verses again to me.

The first few were easy to remember. Finally she had said twenty-three verses. Could she say just two more? Julita closed her eyes. She said one more verse. Then she said another—that made twenty-five verses!

The missionary smiled. "Now I will give out the Bibles." When he came to Julita, he said, "Here is your Bible to keep."

Julita was very happy. Pedro was proud of her.

As they hurried home, Julita said, "Pedro, I will help you learn some verses. Then, at the next Bible meeting, you can win a Bible, too."

Pedro nodded his head. "I will try very hard," he promised.

Maria was watching for them when they left the jungle path.

"God helped me!" called Julita. "God helped me remember the verses. Now we have a Bible—our very own Bible."

A Letter for Robert

"I'll get the mail, Mother," called Robert. He raced out to the front porch just as Mr. Brown, the mailman, came up the steps.

"I have a letter here for Robert Miller," said Mr. Brown.

"A letter for me!" exclaimed Robert.

He took his letter and looked at it. "It's from Grandma," he said, tearing it open.

Mother helped him read some of the words. But he could read most of them himself. He could read, "Robert, we want you to come and visit us." And, "God be with you."

Robert carried his letter around all day. He read it over and over, especially the part that said, "God be with you."

"I know that God is with me," Robert told Mother. "But how does God talk to me? I pray to Him and I know He hears me. But how does He tell me what He wants me to do?"

Instead of answering Robert's question, Mother asked, "You liked the letter Grandma sent you, didn't you?"

"Yes," said Robert, nodding his head. "I always like Grandma's letters."

"Well," said Mother, "God has sent you a letter, too."

"Has He?" asked Robert. "But I haven't seen it. Did Mr. Brown bring it?"

"It is a Book," said Mother. "A very special Book."

Then Robert smiled. "I know what Book you mean," he said. "It's the Bible. But how can the Bible be a letter?"

"Grandma wanted to tell you something," said Mother, "so she wrote you a letter. God wanted to tell you something, too."

"So He sent His Book to me," said Robert. "But I still don't know what He wants me to do."

Mother smiled. "The Bible gives us God's rules. It tells us about the lessons Jesus taught."

Robert thought a minute. Then he said, "God wants me to obey His rules and do the good deeds that Jesus taught us about."

"Yes," said Mother. "And when you read about those things it is the same as if God is telling them to you."

Robert looked at his letter from Grandma. "God be with you," he read. Then he said, "If I know the Bible, then I will know what God wants me to do."

"That's right," said Mother.

"Now I understand," said Robert. "I'm glad God sent me His Book. It is the best letter anybody could ever get!"

The Snowman

"Leave my sled alone," said Corky. "Just because of your new red jacket, you don't own everything."

"I don't want to play with your things," said David, kicking the sled.

"You're the worst brother anybody ever had," said Corky, picking up a handful of snow.

"No, I'm not," said David in a loud voice.

"Yes, you are," said Corky in a louder voice. He threw a snowball at David. But David ducked and the snowball flew past a squirrel sitting on a branch.

"No, I'm not," David shouted.

Mother came out of the house. "What's the fight about?" she asked.

"It's all his fault," said Corky, pointing at David.

"It's your fault," said David, glaring at Corky.

"What is?" asked Mother.

185

Corky looked at David. He looked at Mother. Finally, he said, "I don't remember what we are fighting about."

"Well, then it must not be important," said Mother. "Let's make a snowman to show Father. And without any fighting!"

It was fun to make a snowman. David put stones in for his eyes, nose, and mouth. Corky got him a broom to hold. Mother went inside to get dinner.

"I made a good face for him," said David.

"Well, I got him the broom," said Corky.

David threw a snowball at Corky. Corky pushed David. Soon the boys were rolling around on the ground where the snowman had been.

"I made the snowman," shouted Corky.

"No, I made the snowman," shouted David.

"What snowman?" asked a voice. The boys looked up. It was Father.

"This snowman," said Corky, standing up and pointing. But there was no snowman. Only a broom and a few stones.

David grinned. "Let's make another snowman. You can make the face."

"No," said Corky. "You make the face."

"No, you make the face," said David.

Father laughed. "Remember, no fighting!" he said.

Corky and David laughed, too. "We'll remember," they said.

Lost at The Zoo

Frank and his sister Sarah were ready to go to bed.

"Say your prayers, Curly," Frank told his little dog. Curly put his head down on the edge of the bed. "That's a good dog!"

"Now we'll say *our* prayers," said Sarah.

"I don't have anything to pray about," said Frank, hopping into bed.

"We're going to the zoo tomorrow. You could say, 'Thank you', to God."

"Why?" asked Frank. But he didn't wait for an answer. He turned over and closed his eyes.

The next morning, after breakfast, Mother, Father, Sarah, and Frank went to the zoo. When they got there, Sarah said, "Let's go see the monkeys."

They started down a long path, past some tall giraffes. Frank walked along with his legs stiff, pretending to be a giraffe. He stretched his neck so far forward that he bumped into a little boy. The little boy stared at Frank and then walked away, eating popcorn. Frank wanted some popcorn, too.

"Father," said Frank, without turning around, "can I have some popcorn?"

"What did you say?" asked a strange man.

"Oh, I thought you were my father," mumbled

189

Frank. He looked all around, but didn't see Father anywhere.

He hurried down the path. Soon it divided into two paths. "I don't know which way to go," he said. "I'm lost!"

He ran down one path. Then he turned back and ran down the other.

He kept running and running, but he didn't see Mother or Father or Sarah. "What will I do?" he asked. "Where will I go?"

Frank looked wildly around him. Then he saw a big sign, "Monkey House—this way."

"The monkeys!" he said. "Sarah wanted to see the monkeys. Maybe they went there."

And sure enough, they were at the Monkey House! They had been worried about Frank.

"Are we glad to see you!" said Father.

That night while going to bed, Frank said to Sarah, "Tonight I'm going to say a big, long 'Thank You' prayer. I have a house to live in and food to eat. I have Father and Mother and you and Curly. I have lots of good things."

"But you had all those things last night, too," said Sarah. "And you didn't pray then!"

Frank nodded. "But when I was lost today, I thought, 'What if I didn't have a home?'"

So Frank and Sarah bowed their heads and prayed to God. Curly bowed his head, too.

190

Seeing God

Ruth Ann sat and thought a long time. Finally she said, "I wish I could see God."

"Why?" asked Mother.

"Because then God would be real to me. Something I can't see does not seem real."

Just then the telephone rang. "I'll answer it," said Ruth Ann, getting up.

"Why are you going to answer the phone?" asked Mother.

"Because it rang," answered Ruth Ann. "There, it's ringing again!"

"But I don't *see* it ringing," said Mother.

Ruth Ann, looking puzzled, hurried to answer the telephone. It was Father. "I'll be home early to-night," he said.

Ruth Ann told Mother what Father had said. Then Mother said, "But you didn't *see* Father."

"I didn't have to," said Ruth Ann. "I heard the telephone ring and I heard Father's voice."

"Yes," said Mother. "Do you know what made it possible for you to hear the telephone ring and to hear Father's voice?"

"No, what?" asked Ruth Ann.

"Electricity," answered Mother. "Electricity made the telephone ring. Electricity made it possible for you to hear Father's voice. Did you see the electricity when the telephone rang? Did you see it when you talked with Father?"

Ruth Ann smiled. "No, I didn't."

"Electricity is in the air all around you," said Mother, waving her hand in the air. "Do you see it?"

Ruth Ann looked around. Then she smiled at Mother. "Now I know what you're talking about," she said. "I didn't *see* what made the telephone ring. But the electricity was there. I didn't *see* Father when he talked to me. But I knew he was real."

"Many things are real that we don't see," said Mother.

"Now I know that I don't have to *see* God," said Ruth Ann, "to know that He is real."

Lisa's First Plane Ride

Lisa and Dennis watched a big airplane as it circled above the airport. It looked like a big bird gliding down to earth.

"I've always wanted to go up in a plane," said Dennis, as he watched the plane land and come up the runway. "I would like to be a pilot when I grow up."

Lisa watched the plane, too. But she wished they could go back home. She held tightly to Father's hand.

"Grandmother and Grandfather will meet you when you land at the airport," said Father. "So you don't have anything to be afraid of."

But Lisa was afraid. She had never been up in an airplane before. It was so big, and so noisy!

"As soon as Mother is well," said Father, "we will

194

come and bring you home. Be good children, and obey Grandmother and Grandfather."

"There's our plane," shouted Dennis. He began tugging at Father's arm. "Hurry up. Let's go!"

Before long Dennis and Lisa were sitting in the big plane. Dennis was busy looking at everything. But Lisa could hardly see at all because of the tears in her eyes.

Zoom! The plane ran along the runway. It went faster and faster. Then it went up into the air. It went higher and higher.

What if the plane falls? thought Lisa. Oh, I wish I was home!

Whump! The plane dropped down a bit. Lisa grabbed the arm of her chair and held on tightly. But the plane seemed to be all right again.

"Just an air pocket," said Dennis, looking out the window. "This is fun!"

195

Lisa looked down at the ground, so far below.

"I hope the plane doesn't fall," she kept saying again and again to herself.

Then she saw a small, white church, far, far below on the ground.

All at once Lisa remembered a Bible verse. "When I am afraid, I will trust in Thee."

Lisa smiled and leaned back in her chair. "God is with me up here, too," she told herself.

"There's the city," said Dennis. "We'll soon be at the airport. I hope we can go on another airplane ride soon."

"I hope so, too," said Lisa. "And the next time, I'll remember my verse, 'When I am afraid, I will trust in God.' "

Madonna and Child

By Murillo, Bartolomé Estéban (1617-1682)

In Pitti Gallery, Florence, Italy

Color Photograph by Alinari Brothers, Florence

MARY'S unusually lovely face and the rich, glowing colors make this one of the favorite Madonnas. In art apparently so simple and natural it is often hard to analyze its greatness, yet doesn't the composition gain strength by not being broken into many insignificant lines? We feel a restful simplicity in the picture, because the two figures, Mother and Child, are supreme, with no crowd of details to distract our attention. This same beautiful economy of arrangement and of long, flowing lines, is seen in Murillo's other Madonna, in Volume 7, frontispiece.

Murillo, Spain's greatest religious painter, ranked second in power only to the best artists of Renaissance Italy, such as Raphael. His figures are warmly human and natural. They have an immediate appeal for us, because they seem ready to live and move, as if painted directly from life.

If you look at the picture by Angelico in Volume 7, page 388, you will see the wonderful ease and naturalness Murillo achieved, as compared with the stiff awkwardness of the early painters. Angelico's figures appear to be drawn flat against the background, while Murillo's figures are like human beings, rounded and shaded to stand out from the background, as if you could walk behind them, if you wanted to.

Murillo's characters, as in many other seventeenth century artists, sometimes appear to be sentimental, rather than intensely emotional or spiritual, yet technically he made great progress in achieving freedom and ease in his figures.

Mary has the Spanish type of beauty from Murillo's native city, Seville. She is sweetly human, a person from real life. Notice her beautiful olive coloring and finely-modeled face.

The Child, here, is more idealized than in the other Madonna in Volume 7, frontispiece.

Do you like the colors? Murillo was noted for his rich browns and subtle reds and blue.

Stories
From
Bible Lands

Abraham and The Stars

Abraham stood alone in the dark night. He looked up at the stars so high above him. He said, "I know that the one true God made the stars."

As he looked at the stars, Abraham felt sad. The people in the city where he lived did not worship the one true God. They worshipped the stars as gods. They even built big churches where they worshipped these star gods.

It was not easy for Abraham to worship the one true God in this city. So God told Abraham to go far away to another land.

Abraham and his wife, Sarah, started on the long trip. They walked and walked for many days until they came to a city where God told them to stop. Here they stayed for many years.

Then one day, God said to Abraham, "Leave this place and go to another land. I will show you where it is."

Abraham listened. "I will give you many grandchildren and great-grandchildren and great-great-grandchildren," God said. "All of the people in the world will be helped because of your family."

201

Abraham did not understand these things. He and Sarah were getting old and they did not have children. How could they have grandchildren? But he wanted to do what God told him to do.

Once again Abraham and Sarah started on a long trip. They walked and walked for many days. They did not know where they were going. But God showed Abraham the way.

Finally they came to a place where God told them to stop. God said to Abraham, "I will give all of this fine land to your grandchildren and your great-grandchildren and your great-great-grandchildren."

Then Abraham piled many stones together in a high pile. This was his altar. He stood in front of his altar and prayed to God. He prayed, "Thank You, God, for bringing us safely here to this fine new land."

Years passed.

One night God said to Abraham, "Go outside in the darkness." Abraham went outside. God said, "Look at the stars in the sky. Can you count the stars?"

Abraham looked up. He tried to count the stars. But there were too many. No, he could not count the stars.

Then God said, "I will give you as many grandchildren and great-grandchildren and great-great-grandchildren as there are stars in the sky." This pleased Abraham. He and Sarah were old. And they still did not have children.

But one day, Abraham and Sarah had a little baby son. How pleased they were!

Abraham looked at the stars many times and thought about his little son. He remembered God's promise.

He knew that God would give him many grandchildren and great-grandchildren and great-great-grandchildren, just as He had promised. And Abraham knew that God would give this fine land to them.

But Abraham still did not understand how his family could help all of the families of the world. He did not know what God had planned.

Many years after Abraham had lived, his great-great-grandchildren lived on. Some were ministers and leaders and kings. Many of his family loved God.

And one day, after many, many years, the Baby Jesus was born to Mary. She was married to Joseph, who was a member of Abraham's family. Now Jesus is the Friend and Helper of families everywhere.

Joseph Goes to Egypt

"There they are!" said Joseph to himself. "I see my brothers!" Joseph hurried across the wide field toward his ten big brothers and their sheep. He was glad to see them.

But, his brothers were not glad to see Joseph. They did not like Joseph. When they saw him coming, they said, "Here comes that Joseph. We do not want to listen to him tell us about his dreams."

"In his dreams, he is better than we are," said one of the brothers. "Let's kill him. Then we won't have to listen to him."

"Hello!" called Joseph to his brothers. "Father sent me to find you."

But the brothers were not kind to Joseph. Instead they pulled off the fine coat Father had given to him. They put him down into a deep pit.

Joseph called to his brothers from the deep pit. He did not understand why they were doing this strange thing to him.

But the brothers did not listen. They sat down and ate their lunch.

"Look!" said one of the brothers. "Someone is coming toward us."

They saw men riding on camels slowly coming along the road.

"Those men are merchants," said one of the brothers. "They are going far away to the land of Egypt to buy and to sell."

One of the brothers said, "Let's sell Joseph to them. Then we'll be rid of him."

"Yes, let's do that," agreed the others.

They pulled Joseph out of the deep pit. And they sold their brother to the merchants!

The merchants took Joseph with them to Egypt. There, Joseph became a servant in a rich man's house. Joseph missed his father very much. But he worked hard and always did what was right. He knew that God would take care of him.

The rich man liked Joseph. He put Joseph at the head of his house. But, then, the rich man's wife told her husband a terrible lie about Joseph. Her husband believed her. He sent Joseph to prison.

Even in prison God took care of Joseph. He was put in charge of the other prisoners.

While he was there, a man who had worked for the king was put in the same prison. One night this man had a strange dream. He told Joseph about it.

"God helps me to understand dreams," Joseph said. "Your dream means that in three days you will go back to work for the king again."

And in three days, it happened as Joseph had said it would.

Two years went by, and one night the king had a dream. Then, his servant thought about Joseph. He told the king, "There is a man in prison who understands dreams."

So the king sent for Joseph. He told Joseph his dream.

Joseph said, "God has helped me to understand your dream. For seven years, there will be more than enough food for all. Then for seven years, there will be very little food. You must find a good man to save some of the food during the first seven years."

"You are a good man," the king said to Joseph. "God takes care of you. I will put you in charge of all Egypt. You must save some food now. Then we will have it when we need it."

Joseph was put in charge of all Egypt. Everyone but the king had to obey Joseph.

"Father would be proud of me now," said Joseph. "I was only a servant. Now I am in charge of the country. God has taken good care of me."

Joseph's Brothers Go to Egypt

An Egyptian man bowed low before the king. "Please sell me some food?" he begged. "Mine is gone, and nothing grows. My family is hungry."

"See Joseph," said the king, with a wave of his hand. "Joseph is in charge of all the food."

The man hurried to Joseph and bowed low before him. "May I buy food?" he begged. "My food is gone. My family is hungry."

"Yes," said Joseph, "You may buy food—buy all that you need."

No food would grow in all of Egypt, so the people came to ask Joseph for food. Food would not grow in other countries, either. People from those countries asked Joseph for food, too. Joseph was glad to give them food.

One day, as Joseph was distributing food, he saw some men come in whom he thought he knew. He wondered, "Where have I seen those men before?"

The men came closer. All at once, Joseph knew. "They are my brothers!" he said.

The ten men came up to Joseph and bowed low before him. "Oh, sir, may we buy food?" they begged. "We do not have any. Our families are hungry."

The brothers did not know Joseph!

Joseph thought of the last time he had seen his brothers. They had sold him to merchants who were on their way to Egypt.

Joseph said in a hard voice, "You are spies! You have come to see how you can make war on Egypt."

"Oh, no!" said his brothers. "We are not spies. We are all sons of one father. He is at home with our youngest brother. Oh, no, sir! We are not spies!"

"You must show me that what you say is true," said Joseph. "One of you must stay here in prison while the others go home. Bring back your youngest brother with you."

The brothers were afraid of this man who was so powerful in Egypt. So nine of the ten brothers took food and went home.

After many months, the brothers needed more food. Once again they went on the long trip to Egypt. And this time they took their youngest brother, Benjamin, with them.

When they came to Egypt, Joseph said, "I will keep your youngest brother here. He will be a servant in the palace."

At once the brothers said, "Oh, please, do not keep our youngest brother. Our father loves him very much."

One of the brothers said, "I will stay here in Benjamin's place. Please let him go home."

Then, Joseph knew that now the brothers were good men. He knew they would not sell Benjamin as they had sold him.

So Joseph looked at his brothers. He looked from one to another. Then he said to them, "I am Joseph, your brother."

The brothers stared at this great man. Joseph! They could not believe it.

"Do not be afraid," said Joseph. "I am really your brother. You sold me to the Egyptian merchants many years ago. But I have forgiven you. God wanted me to be here to save enough food for everyone. I can take care of you now."

Then Joseph threw his arms around his brothers. They all talked at once! How exciting it was to see each other again!

"Go home," said Joseph. "Bring our father here. And bring your families, too."

So the brothers went home and brought their father and their families to Egypt as Joseph had asked. They were very happy in their new home.

"God sent me to Egypt," said Joseph. "He has made me a leader in this country. Now I can take care of my father and my brothers. This was God's plan."

A Good Leader

"What is that?" asked the Egyptian princess, pointing to a basket floating on the water near the tall grass.

"Go and bring it to me," she told one of her maids.

The maid stepped into the water. She waded out to get the basket. When the maid brought it to her, the princess exclaimed, "There's a baby in it!"

The baby was frightened and cried loudly. Carefully the princess lifted him out of the basket and rocked him in her arms.

"It must be a little Hebrew baby," she said.

The Hebrew people were slaves of the Egyptian people. The princess knew that her father, the Egyptian king, had said that all Hebrew baby boys must be thrown into the river and drowned. He was afraid that some day there would be too many Hebrew people. Then, they might fight with the Egyptians.

"I like this little baby," said the princess. "I do not want him to be drowned. He will be my son. I will name him Moses."

The princess was right. Moses was a Hebrew boy. But he lived just like an Egyptian prince. He grew up in the palace. He had fine clothes and the best food.

Many servants did what he told them to do. He had everything he wanted.

But, one day, Moses saw something that made him very angry. He saw an Egyptian man hurting a Hebrew slave. Although Moses had grown up among the Egyptians, he knew that it was not right for them to hurt the Hebrew people.

He tried to stop the Egyptian man by hitting him. He hit the man so hard that he killed him.

Moses was frightened and very sorry. He had to leave the palace. He had to leave Egypt. He went off into the mountains far away and became a shepherd.

He took care of many sheep year after year. He walked with his sheep through the mountains and down into the valleys.

One day, as Moses was with his sheep in the mountains, he saw a bush that was on fire. He hurried to it. Then he stopped and stared. The bush was burning, but it did not burn up! Moses could not understand this strange fire.

Then he heard a voice. It was God's voice!

God said, "Moses, I want you to go back to Egypt. There, the Hebrew slaves have to work too hard. They are sad. You must lead them away from Egypt."

Moses went back to Egypt. A new king lived in the palace now.

Moses went to see him. Moses said, "Let the

Hebrew people go away from Egypt. Let them go and worship God."

"Who is God?" asked the king. "I do not care about your God. No, the Hebrew slaves cannot go."

Moses asked many times, but always the king said, "No, they cannot go." Each time the king refused God sent trouble to the Egyptian people. Finally the king said, "Yes, they may go."

At once, in the middle of the night, the Hebrew people started out. They followed Moses as he led them away from Egypt.

They walked and walked until they came to a wide sea. They did not know what to do. They could not go across the sea.

But, God told Moses just what to do. Moses lifted up a long stick and held it out over the wide sea. The wind began to blow. It blew and blew and blew. The wind blew the water back until there was a wide path of dry land across the sea.

Then, Moses led his people through the sea to the other side.

After everyone was safe, the wind stopped blowing and the water covered the dry path.

Now the Hebrew people were safe from the Egyptian king. Moses had led them safely away from Egypt, just as God had told him to do.

God's Rules

"I am so tired walking!" said a little girl. "I wonder where Moses is leading us."

"We have walked for miles and miles," said her brother. "And still Moses keeps on going."

"Oh, look at that big mountain," said the girl. "How high it is!"

Moses called out to all the people, "God wants us to stop here. Put up your tents."

The people sat down on the ground. It felt good to rest. They had walked for a long time.

Moses walked toward the high, rocky mountain and climbed up the steep side.

God talked to Moses there. He said, "Tell the people that I have taken care of them. I have kept them safe. If they will obey My rules, I will always be with them."

Moses climbed down the mountain. He called the people together and told them what God had said.

Then the people answered, "All that God wants us to do, we will do."

217

Moses went back to the mountain. God said, "In three days, I will talk to the people. Put a barrier up around this mountain. They must not touch the mountain. Then tell the people to make themselves neat and clean and get ready to listen to Me. I will come in a thick cloud."

So Moses had a fence put up around the mountain. The people made themselves neat. The mothers washed the clothes. Everyone wanted to be ready to listen to God.

On the third morning, the people were still in their tents. A thick cloud came down and covered the top of the mountain.

Rolls of thunder sounded all around. The people looked out of their tents. They saw flashes of lightning zig-zagging through the dark sky.

Then the mighty trumpet of God blew loud and long. The people were frightened.

But Moses led them out of the camp and to the foot of the mountain.

Great clouds of smoke rose up from the mountain. Then the whole mountain shook.

The people stood still and waited.

God spoke to them. He said, "I have taken care of you. Do not worship any other Gods but Me. Do not make idols and worship them. Do not swear. Remember to keep the Lord's Day holy. Love and obey your fathers and mothers. Do not kill. Always think clean thoughts. Do not steal. Do not tell lies. Be happy with what you have."

The people listened as God spoke. They heard the crash of thunder and the sound of the trumpet. They saw streaks of lightning in the sky. They saw smoke rising from the mountain.

The people moved away from the mountain. They did not like to stand so close.

They said to Moses, "We are afraid. You go and talk to God. Then come and tell us what He says."

So Moses climbed up the mountain in the thick darkness. God was there. Moses stayed on the mountain with God a long time.

God gave Moses many rules. Then God wrote His rules on two flat stones. He wrote on both sides of the stones. Then He gave the stones to Moses.

Moses carried the stones carefully down the steep, rocky mountain. He said, "These are God's rules. He has given them to us so that we can please Him. If we obey God's rules, He will always be with us."

Ruth Is Kind

"We are so hungry, Mother," Naomi's two sons said to her. "Please give us something to eat."

"But I have nothing to give you," Naomi said. "There is no rain. Food will not grow in our land. Everyone is hungry."

"Lets us go to another land where there is plenty of food," said Father.

"Yes, let's go," said Naomi and the boys. So the family packed for a trip. They moved to the faraway land of Moab.

Everything was strange in this new land. Most of the people had never heard of the true God. But the boys' Mother and Father said, "Even here we will always obey the Lord God."

The family was very happy for awhile. But then the Father became sick and died.

The two boys grew up. They married beautiful women of Moab. One son married Orpah. The other married Ruth.

After a time the two sons died. How sad and lonely Naomi was! She began to think of her old home. She called Ruth and Orpah to her. "There is food in my land again. I want to go home," she said.

Orpah and Ruth walked down the road with Naomi. "We will go with you and help you," they both said kindly.

"No," said Naomi. "You must go back. My land is far away. You will be happier with your own people."

Orpah kissed Naomi and went back home.

Then Naomi said to Ruth, "See. Orpah has gone back to her people and her gods. You must go, too."

But Ruth said, "Please don't ask me to leave you. Where you go, I will go. Where you live, I will live. Your people shall be my people, and your God my God."

It was a long trip to Naomi's home town. How glad Naomi's old friends were to see her! They were sorry to hear about her trouble.

Ruth and Naomi had no money to buy food. "It is time for the ripe grain to be cut," said Ruth. "Let me go to the fields and find food."

"Go, my daughter," said Naomi.

So Ruth went into a big field to pick up grain which the workers did not need. A rich man named Boaz came to look at his field. He saw Ruth working there. "Who is this young woman?" he asked.

"She is Ruth," the workers said. "She came from Moab with Naomi. She is getting food for Naomi."

222

Then Boaz said to Ruth, "Do not go to any other field for food. But stay here and pick up grain. When you are thirsty, you may drink our water."

"Why are you so kind to me?" asked Ruth.

"I have heard how you left your people and your gods," said Boaz. "You have been very kind to Naomi. May God, whom you now trust, show kindness to you."

Day after day Ruth worked in the field of Boaz. He was very kind to her. He helped her gather much food to take home to Naomi.

One day Boaz said to Ruth, "I love you very much. I want you to be my wife."

So they were married. How happy they were together. Later, God sent them a baby boy. They named him Obed.

When Obed grew up, he was the grandfather of King David.

And many, many years later, God sent Jesus into the world through the family of King David.

God Talks to Samuel

Samuel stood in the doorway of the Tabernacle. He looked off down the road.

"Soon Mother and Father will be coming to see me," he said happily. "They will be surprised to see how tall I've grown."

Eli, the old minister smiled. "You grow taller and taller every year," he said.

"Every year when Mother brings me a new coat, the old one is too short," said Samuel.

Eli said, "Your mother and father must be very proud of you. You do many things to help here at the Tabernacle."

"I like it here," said Samuel. "I like to open the big doors every morning. And I like to light the lamps at night."

"I don't know how I would get along without you," said Eli. "I wish my sons wanted to help here in God's House, too."

Samuel looked off down the road again. His mother and father came once every year. They came to worship God and to see Samuel. How glad Samuel was to see them! And how glad they were to see him.

Mother brought Samuel a fine new coat. And it

fit just right! "How did you know how big I was?" asked Samuel.

Mother laughed. "Oh, I just knew."

When they left, Samuel stood in the doorway of the Tabernacle and waved good-by. Then, he went back into the Tabernacle. He had many things to do.

Samuel was always busy. Every morning, he opened the big doors of the Tabernacle. Then, people could come in and worship God. He polished lamps and dusted furniture. He swept the floors and lit the lamps. He helped Eli all day long.

One night Samuel went to bed early. Eli had gone to bed, too. Samuel was almost asleep, when he heard a voice call, "Samuel!"

"Here I am," answered Samuel. He jumped up and ran into Eli's room. He thought Eli had called him.

"I did not call you," said Eli. "Lie down again and go back to sleep."

So Samuel went back to bed. But before long, he heard a voice calling, "Samuel! Samuel!"

Samuel jumped up and ran to Eli. "Here I am," he said. "You called me."

"I did not call you, Samuel," said Eli. "Go back to your bed."

Samuel lay down on his bed again. The voice called, "Samuel!"

Once more Samuel ran into Eli's room. "Here I am," he said. "Did you call me?"

226

Then Eli knew that God was calling Samuel. "Go back and lie down," he said. "And when you hear the voice call your name again, you must say, "Speak, Lord. I am ready to listen to You."

Samuel went back to bed. Soon he heard the voice of God call, "Samuel! Samuel!"

He answered, "Speak, for I am listening."

Then God said, "Eli's sons have done many bad things. So Eli's family will not be allowed to work for me in My House."

Samuel lay awake all night, thinking about what God had told him. In the morning he got up and opened the big doors.

Samuel did not want to tell Eli what God had said. But Eli called, "Samuel."

"Here I am," answered Samuel.

"What did God tell you?" asked Eli. "Do not hide anything from me."

So Samuel told Eli what God had said. Eli was sad to hear this, but he said, "God will do what is right."

Samuel grew up in the Tabernacle. Many times God talked to him. God was with Samuel and loved him.

The Brave Shepherd Boy

"One, two, three, four, five . . ." David counted
his sheep many times a day. Yes, all the sheep were
there. He had led them safely through a wide field
and up a steep, rocky path. Now they were drinking
water from a quiet brook.

David picked up a small, flat stone and put it in
his slingshot.

"I must be ready to defend and protect my sheep,"
he said.

He swung the slingshot around and aimed at a tree.
Zing! The stone flew through the air and hit the tree.
David knew how to use it well.

One day a big bear came creeping close to the
sheep. It picked up a little lamb in its mouth and
started to carry it away. But David had seen the
bear. *Zing!* A stone flew through the air and the bear
fell dead. The little lamb was safe again.

On another day, a fierce-looking lion tried to carry
a sheep away. But David, with his club in his hand,
rushed at the lion and killed it. Now the sheep was
safe.

"I am not afraid of the bear or the lion," said David.

229

"I am not afraid, because God helps and takes care of me."

David stayed out in the quiet hills most of the time. But a great war began in his country. Three of his brothers went to be soldiers in the army.

One day David's father said, "David, go and see how your brothers are getting along. Take this corn and bread to them."

David left his sheep with a keeper. Very early in the morning he started out to find the army. The camp was up on a mountain, and just across the valley on a nearby mountain, was the camp of the other army.

Even though there were many soldiers in the camp, David soon found his brothers. He gave them the food that their father had sent.

David was talking to his brothers when he heard someone shouting in loud voice. He looked around to see who it was.

There, standing down in the valley between the two armies, was a giant! This fierce-looking giant was over nine feet tall. He called in a loud voice, "Send someone to fight with me."

The soldiers told David, "Goliath, the giant, comes out every morning and every evening. He calls for a man to go and fight with him. King Saul is looking for a soldier who will go, but everyone is afraid. Goliath is so big!"

David looked down into the valley at the giant. "Why should he think that he is stronger than we are?" asked David. "God will help us."

David went to King Saul. "I will go and fight with Goliath," he said.

"Oh, no," said King Saul. "You are only a shepherd boy and he is a man of war!"

David said, "I have killed a bear and a lion. I can kill a giant, too. God will be with me and help me."

David took his slingshot and five small stones. When Goliath saw David coming, he was angry. "Are you coming to fight with me?" he shouted. "You are too small!"

David called out, "You are coming to fight me with a sword and a spear. I am coming to fight you in the name of the Lord."

David put one of the stones in his slingshot. He ran toward the giant and threw the stone. *Zing!* The stone flew through the air and Goliath fell dead.

Then, all the other soldiers in Goliath's army were afraid. They ran away.

"How brave David is!" everyone said.

But David only said, "God is my Helper."

Best Friends

David went to live in the king's palace. Not so long ago, he had been a shepherd boy! Now he lived in the king's palace and ate at the king's table.

He liked to live in the palace because his best friend, Jonathan, lived there, too. Jonathan was King Saul's son. He liked David so much that he gave his own coat as a gift to David.

God planned for David to be the next king, instead of Jonathan. But Jonathan didn't mind. He was glad to know that his best friend would some day be the king.

David helped King Saul in many ways. One day, the king began to act strangely. He said unkind words to David. He acted unkindly, too. King Saul was sick. That is why he wanted to hurt David.

Jonathan talked to his father. He said, "David has done many things to help you. You should not hurt him."

"That is right," agreed King Saul. "I will try not to hurt David any more."

But the king forgot. One day, he grew so angry that he said to Jonathan, "Find David and bring him here. I will kill him."

233

Jonathan did not want his good friend to die. He hurried to find David.

He told him that King Saul planned to kill him. "You must go away," he said. "God will be between you and me, between your children and my children forever."

Sadly the two friends said good-by.

Many years passed. There were many wars in the land. King Saul and Jonathan had to fight in battle many times.

Then one day, David heard the sad news. King Saul and Jonathan had been killed in the war. David was very unhappy. "Jonathan was my very best friend," he said sadly.

Now, David became king in part of the kingdom. Many more years passed. Finally, David became king over all the country where Saul had ruled.

Although Jonathan had died many years before, David had not forgotten him. He asked his servants, "Is there anyone still living who worked for King Saul?"

"Yes," they said. "One of his old servants is still living."

"Bring him to me!" said David.

They brought the old servant to David.

"Are any of King Saul's family still alive?" David asked the servant.

"Yes," he answered. "Jonathan's son lives near here.

He is lame and life is very hard for him."

"Jonathan's son!" cried David.

"He was only five years old when we heard that Jonathan had been killed in the war," said the servant. "It was not safe for him to stay where he was, so his nurse took him away. While they were escaping the little boy fell and got hurt. Now he is lame in both feet."

"That is so long ago!" said David. "He must be a man now. Bring him to me."

Jonathan's son was surprised to be called to King David's palace. He came at once and knelt in front of David.

"Do not be afraid," said David. "Your father was my best friend. I will take care of you. I will give you all the land that was your father's."

Jonathan's son did not know what to say.

David went on, "You must eat your meals at my table and let me be your friend."

Jonathan's son ate at the king's table, just as David had done many years before. Every time David looked at Jonathan's son, he thought, "I am glad that I can help Jonathan's son. I will never forget my best friend, Jonathan."

Building God's House

In all the land there was no House of God. There was no House where the people could worship God.

So King Solomon said, "I will build a House of God—a place to worship God."

There was much to do before they could start building God's House. First Solomon wrote to the king of a nearby country.

Solomon's letter said, "Your country has the finest trees. I want to use some of your cedar trees to build a Temple, a place where we can worship God."

"I will have my servants cut down the finest trees," said this king. "They will take the trees carefully down the mountain and float them down the sea to King Solomon's country. I will be glad to send the cedar wood, then I will be helping to build God's House, too."

The very best workmen made many stone blocks for the Temple. They made the stone blocks of different sizes and shapes. And each stone block had to be just the right size and just the right shape.

When the wood and the stone blocks were ready, it was time for the builders to begin. King Solomon chose a high mound in the city of Jerusalem on which to build the temple. They built the walls of the very best stone blocks. They made the floor and the roof of fine wood. Then they covered the walls with beautiful cedar wood.

King Solomon searched everywhere for the very best workmen to do special carving in the Temple. On the cedar wood, they carved pictures of beautiful flowers and palm trees. They carved pictures of cherubims, which were angels who looked like boys and girls.

How fine the Temple looked! But it was not finished yet!

Next, they covered the carving with thin sheets of gold. The gold fitted closely over the carved pictures and made them look as if they had been carved in gold. In front of the temple, they put two large pillars of brass. The pillars were decorated with flowers and ropes, all made out of brass.

Now the beautiful Temple shone with brightness!

It had taken seven long years to build the Temple. Many thousands of men had worked on it. Now that it was finished the workmen were very happy.

Solomon built many other buildings, too. He sent to faraway countries to get material for these buildings. Many ships brought chests and bundles of the very best. They brought rich-looking cloth for curtains. They brought ivory to build a gleaming white throne. They brought beautiful blue peacocks to walk about in the pretty gardens. They brought silver and precious jewels to trim the furniture and make it more beautiful.

But the finest building of all was God's House.

When it was finished, King Solomon called the ministers together. They stood in front of the beautiful Temple.

Solomon talked to them and to the people. He said, "God has taken care of our people for many, many years. Now, we have been able to build this beautiful Temple where we can come to worship Him."

Then Solomon lifted his hands up toward Heaven and prayed to God. He prayed, "Oh God, You are the one true God. You keep all of Your promises to the people who obey You. Hear my prayer today— take care of our people, keep us safe, forgive us when we do wrong and, thank You, God, for taking care of us."

The One True God

Elijah walked bravely into the palace of the wicked king, Ahab. "You do not obey the one true God," Elijah said to the king. "So there will be no rain in your land until I say so."

And for three years no rain fell in the land. The rivers were dry. Nothing grew. The people were hungry and thirsty.

"Elijah made this trouble," said King Ahab. "I will find him and kill him."

The wicked king looked everywhere for Elijah. But he could not find him. God was taking care of him.

One day God spoke to Elijah. "Go to the king," He said. "I will send rain again."

When the king Ahab saw Elijah, he asked angrily, "Are you the man who brings trouble to our land?"

"I am not the one who brings trouble," said Elijah. "It is you and your family. You have forgotten God. You worship Baal. He is not God. He is only an idol."

This made King Ahab very angry.

Then Elijah said to the king, "Tell all of the people and the priests of Baal to meet me on the mountain."

So everyone climbed to the top of the mountain. Elijah said to them, "You must make up your minds.

You cannot have two gods. If the Lord is the one true God, obey Him. But if Baal is God, obey him."

The people did not know what to say.

"Let us have a contest," said Elijah. "Let the priests of Baal put an offering on an altar. Let them pray to Baal. Then I will put an offering on another altar. I will pray to the Lord God. The one who sends fire from Heaven will be our God."

"That is a fair plan," said the people.

So the priests of Baal put their offering on an altar. From morning until noon they cried, "Oh, Baal, hear us!" But no fire came.

At noon Elijah said to them, "Why don't you call a little louder. Baal might be away on a trip. Maybe he is asleep. If he is talking, he could not hear you."

So the priests tried harder. They shouted louder and louder to Baal. They jumped up and down. But evening came, and there was no fire.

Then Elijah called the people around him. He put his offering on an altar made of twelve big stones.

Elijah wanted to make it hard for a fire to start. So he said, "Pour some water on the altar."

Splash! The water ran over the offering and trickled down into a ditch around the altar. Three times they poured the water.

Now, everything was ready. Elijah lifted his hands and prayed. "Lord," he said, "show us all today that You are the one true God."

242

Flash! Fire came from heaven! It burned the offering, and it burned the stones of the altar!

When the people saw this wonderful thing, they cried, "The Lord, He is God!"

Then Elijah said to King Ahab, "You must start home. A hard rain is coming. Your chariot might get stuck in the mud."

So, King Ahab climbed into his chariot.

Soon the sky began to fill with black clouds. The wind blew hard. Raindrops fell.

The people began running to get out of the rain. Elijah ran, too. He caught up with the king's chariot. He ran faster than the horses that pulled the king's chariot. He came to the city first.

How glad the people were to have the good cool rain. "Now we will not be hungry or thirsty again," they said. "The one true God has sent the good rain to us."

God Takes Care of Daniel

"This rich food and wine is not good for us," said Daniel to his three friends.

"The king thinks it will make us strong," said one of them. "He thinks that if we eat this food we will be able to learn more."

"The other boys here in the school all eat it," said another.

"But God does not want us to eat it," said Daniel. "I will not eat it."

"We don't want to eat it either," said the third friend. "But we must obey the king."

"God is stronger than the king," said Daniel. "He will take care of us."

"Daniel," said one of the friends, "Why don't you see the prince who takes care of us? Ask him about our food."

So, Daniel went to find the prince. He said, "Please give us plain food and water. This food is not good for us."

"I would like to, Daniel," answered the prince. "But I am afraid to. The king would not like it if you got sick."

"Let us try it," said Daniel. "For ten days, let us eat plain food and drink water. If we are not as well as the other boys, then you may feed us what you want to."

So for ten days the prince gave Daniel and his three friends plain food and water.

At the end of the ten days, the four boys were stronger and healthier than any of the other boys in the school.

So Daniel and his three friends did not have to eat the rich food and wine.

One day the king sent for all the boys in the school. He asked them many difficult questions. Then he said, "Daniel and his three friends are ten times smarter than any man in my whole land."

This pleased Daniel. But he knew that it was God who helped him learn so much.

Every day Daniel opened his windows and knelt down in front of them. Then he prayed to God and thanked Him. Three times a day Daniel did this.

Now, there was a new king in the land. He liked Daniel. He made Daniel his first helper. This made many men angry. They all wanted to be the king's first helper.

"How can we get Daniel into trouble?" they asked. "He is too smart and too good."

The men made a plan. Then they went to the king. "Oh King, make a new law," they said. "If someone prays to anyone else but you, put him in a lions' den."

246

So the king made the new law. But Daniel would not stop praying to God. He prayed three times a day, just as he always had.

The men ran to the king. "Oh King," they said, "Daniel will not obey your law. He must be put into the den of hungry lions."

Now the king was sorry that he had made the law. But it could not be changed.

So, Daniel was put into the lions' den.

The king said, "Your God can save you." That night the king could not sleep. He did not eat. He would not listen to any music.

Early in the morning he ran to the lions' den. He called out, "Daniel, is your God able to save you from the lions?"

Daniel said, "Oh King, God sent His angel. He shut the lions' mouths. They have not hurt me at all."

How glad the king was! "Take Daniel out of the lions' den," he ordered.

Daniel was not hurt. God had taken care of him.

"Everyone must fear Daniel's God," said the king. "He is the living God and He will live forever. He took care of Daniel, and He will take care of us."

The Savior Is Born

Mary sang to herself as she worked around the house. She helped her mother clean the house. She watered the flowers in the garden. She sewed her new dress—her wedding dress. Soon she would be marrying Joseph, the carpenter.

All at once, an angel stood in front of her.

"God is with you," said the angel.

Mary had never seen an angel before.

"Do not be afraid," he said. "You will have a Baby. Name Him Jesus. He will be God's Son, and He will be a King forever."

How surprised Mary was!

The angel went to Joseph, too. The angel said, "Mary will have a Baby. Name Him Jesus. He will save the people from their sins." Joseph was surprised, too.

Mary and Joseph were married. Many weeks went by. Then, everyone in Joseph's family had to go to Bethlehem to be counted.

Joseph and Mary went, too. But so many other people had come to Bethlehem that Joseph could not find a room for Mary. Finally he found a place to stay in a stable near an inn.

Later that night the little Baby was born. Mary wrapped Him warmly and laid Him in a manger.

Mary and Joseph named the Baby, Jesus, just as the angel had told them to do.

The night was very quiet. Then Mary and Joseph heard voices outside. Shepherds came into the stable.

Very quietly they walked over to Jesus. They smiled at the little Baby. Then, one by one, they knelt in front of Him. They bowed their heads and prayed. They knew that this little Baby was God's Son.

The shepherds stood up. They smiled at Mary and Joseph. Then, just as quietly as they had come, they went out into the night.

Far away to the East, lived wise men who studied the stars. One night, as they looked at the sky, they saw a bright star.

"That is the brightest star I have ever seen," said one of these wise men. "God must have sent it to tell us that the new King of the Hebrew people has been born."

So, the wise men started out on their camels to look for the new King. They rode a long, long way.

Finally, they came to the city of Jerusalem, where many Hebrew people lived. They asked, "Where is the new King, who has just been born? We have seen His star in the East."

No one knew anything about this new King. Even King Herod did not know. He asked many teachers and holy men about this new King.

The holy men told him, "Our holy books tell us that a King will be born in Bethlehem."

King Herod said to the wise men, "Go to Bethlehem and find this new King. Then come and tell me where He is, so that I can see Him, too."

It was night, but the wise men started at once for Bethlehem. As they rode on their camels, they looked up at the stars. And there, shining brightly, high above them, was the same star they had seen in the East!

They followed the star to Bethlehem. It shone high over a little house—the very house where Mary and Joseph and Jesus were staying!

The wise men went inside and saw little Jesus, sitting on Mary's lap. The wise men knelt in front of Him. They thanked God for sending the new King.

Then they gave Jesus the gifts they had brought. They gave Jesus precious gold, sweet-smelling incense, and soothing myrrh. These were the finest gifts, fit for the greatest King!

That night, the wise men had a dream. In the dream, God told them, "Do not go back to the wicked King Herod. He wants to kill Jesus."

The wise men went home another way and God kept Jesus safe. As the wise men rode home on their camels, they said to each other, "We have seen God's Son. He will be a King forever."

Jesus in God's House

Tap, tap, tap! went Joseph's hammer. Then he put it down on the bench beside him. "There," he said, "that job is done."

He looked across the little shop where he worked. Jesus was busy at another bench. "We will not work any more today," said Joseph. "We must get ready to leave early in the morning."

They were going to Jerusalem for the Passover. This was a special time when the people thought about God. They remembered the wonderful way that He had taken care of the Hebrew people. Jesus was twelve years old now, and could go to the Passover in Jerusalem.

Early the next morning, they started for Jerusalem. It was a long way to walk. It took them three whole days. But, they did not mind.

Many other people were going to Jerusalem, too. Jesus and Mary and Joseph walked along with them. When it was time to eat, they stopped and had a picnic lunch beside the road. When night came, they lay down on the ground and pulled their coats around them. They went to sleep under the starry sky.

When they came to the great city of Jerusalem,

253

they hurried to God's House. How beautiful it was! Jesus looked and looked. Then, He bowed His head and prayed to God.

In God's House were many teachers. They studied God's Word and taught the people about God.

For a whole week Jesus' family stayed in Jerusalem. Jesus went to God's House often to listen and learn, and to worship God.

After the Passover, the people started back to their homes. Friends and neighbors walked along, side by side, talking about the Passover.

Sometimes, the boys walked with their mothers. Sometimes, they walked with their fathers. Sometimes, the boys walked together.

"Jesus must be walking with Joseph," thought Mary.

"Jesus must be walking with the other boys," thought Joseph.

When night came, they asked people, "Have you seen Jesus?"

"No," their friends answered. "We haven't seen Him. He has not been with us."

Nobody had seen Jesus all day!

"Joseph," said Mary, "we must go back to Jerusalem. Jesus must still be there."

"Yes," answered Joseph, looking very worried. "That is what we must do."

So Joseph and Mary began the long walk back to

Jerusalem. It took them a whole day to get there. They went up and down the streets, looking for Jesus. But they could not find Him anywhere.

Then, they remembered that Jesus loved to visit God's House. They hurried to God's House.

There was Jesus talking to the teachers and asking questions about God.

"How can this Boy know so much about God?" the teachers asked each other. "He is only twelve years old."

Mary and Joseph were surprised at the many things that Jesus knew. But they could not forget how worried they had been.

"We have been looking all over for You," said Mary. "We have been very sad and worried."

Jesus asked Mary and Joseph, "Why did you look for Me? It is now time for Me to begin my work for God."

Then Mary and Joseph and Jesus went home to Nazareth. Jesus always obeyed Mary and Joseph. He always obeyed God. And He always loved to go to God's House.

A Little Sick Girl

A little girl lay in her bed. She was quiet and still. Her mother washed her face with cool water. Her father sat beside the bed.

"She is so sick, Jairus," said her mother. "If only someone could help her."

"I have heard that Jesus has made many people well," said her father. "I will go and ask Him to come."

"Please hurry and find Him," begged the sad mother. "If He does not come soon, our daughter will die."

Jairus hurried down the road to look for Jesus. He saw a crowd of people on the shore of the lake. Jesus was standing in the middle of the crowd. He was teaching the people.

"How can I ever get close enough to talk to Jesus?" thought Jairus.

He pushed his way through the crowd. "Please let me through," he said. "I must talk to Jesus."

He kept moving until he reached Jesus. Jairus fell on his knees before Him.

"My only daughter is dying," he said. "Please come with me. I know You can make her well."

Jesus wanted to help the sad father. "I will come with you," He said.

But, it was hard to hurry. So many people kept crowding around Jesus.

A woman who had been very sick for many years was in the crowd, too. This woman had spent all of her money trying to get better. But, no doctor could make her well.

"If I could only touch Jesus," she said. "I know He could help me."

When Jesus walked by with Jairus, the woman reached out and touched the hem of Jesus' coat. At once, she was well again.

Jesus stopped. "Who touched me?" He asked.

The woman was afraid. But she knew that she could not hide. "I touched you because I wanted to be well," she said.

"Go your way," said Jesus. "Because you believed in Me, you have been made well."

Jairus was glad that the sick woman was well. But he wished that Jesus would hurry. My little girl cannot live much longer, he thought.

Then, a man came running. "Jairus, you do not need to bother Jesus," he said. "Your little girl is dead."

Jesus said to the sad father, "Do not be afraid.

Only believe in Me, and she will be made well."

At last, they came to Jairus' house. Many people were outside. They were crying because the little girl was dead.

"Why are you crying?" asked Jesus. "The child is not dead. She is sleeping."

The people laughed at Jesus. They knew that the sick girl had died.

Jesus went to the room where the little girl lay in bed. Her mother and father and three of Jesus' friends followed Him.

Jesus took the little girl by the hand. He said, "Little girl, get up."

And the little girl got up. She walked. She was alive again!

"Give her something to eat," Jesus said. "And do not tell anyone what has happened."

But, the happy family could not keep such a great secret! "Did you hear what a wonderful thing Jesus had done?" they told everyone. "Our little girl was dead. But Jesus made her live again!"

Peter Walks on The Water

Jesus had been busy teaching a crowd of people all day. Now, He was sending everyone home.

"It is getting late," said one of Jesus' friends.

"I am tired after such a busy day," said another.

"Take your boat," Jesus said to Peter and His other helpers. "Row across the lake without me."

"But, we do not want to leave you here," said His helpers.

"I am going up on the mountain alone to pray," Jesus said. "I will come to you later." He turned away and walked to the mountain alone.

So, Peter and the other men got into the boat. They rowed out into the lake. Soon they were in the middle of the lake.

Then the sky filled with black clouds. The stars were gone. *Ooooooo*. The wind blew hard. *Wham!* Big waves smashed against the boat. They were in a bad storm.

The men rowed as hard as they could. But they could not get any closer to the shore. The wind and the waves tossed the boat this way and that way. The men were tired. They did not think they could

row any more. They were afraid that the big waves would overturn the boat. Then they would all drown.

"If only Jesus had come with us," they said, "He could have helped us."

All at once the men saw something moving on top of the waves. It came closer and closer to the boat.

"What is it?" the men wondered.

"It looks like a man," said one. "But no man could walk on the water."

The men were very frightened. "It is a ghost!" they said.

Then, they heard a voice which they knew belonged to Jesus. "Do not be afraid," He said, "it is I."

How glad the men were to hear the voice of their Friend, Jesus. "Now that Jesus is here, we do not have to be afraid any more," they said.

When Peter saw Jesus walking on the water, he wanted to try it, too. He said, "Lord, if it is You, tell me to come to You on the water."

"Come," Jesus said.

Peter climbed over the side of the boat. He stepped out on top of the water. He looked into Jesus' kind face. He walked on the water, too.

Ooooooo. The wind blew hard. *Wham!* Big waves smashed against the boat. Peter forgot to look at Jesus. All at once, he was afraid. When he looked down at the water, he began to sink.

"Lord, save me!" Peter cried.

Jesus caught Peter and pulled him up out of the water. "You do not trust Me enough, Peter," He said. "Why did you think I would not take care of you?"

Jesus helped Peter climb back into the boat. Then, Jesus stepped into the boat. As soon as he did, the storm stopped. The wind was quiet. The lake was smooth and still. The black clouds were gone. The stars were shining again.

It was easy for the men to row, now. They soon came to the other side of the lake.

The men in the boat thought about the wonderful thing that they had just seen. They said to Jesus, "Now we know that You are the Son of God!"

A Poor Blind Man

A blind man sat by the side of the road. There was no work for him to do in the town where he lived. So, he called out to the people as they walked by. "I am a poor blind man," he cried. "I'm hungry. Please give me money so I can buy bread."

He sat and held his hand out in front of him, hoping that someone would give him money. He could feel the round, hard coins in his hand. He wished that he could see the people who gave him money.

How dark it was for him! He had been blind all of his life.

He could feel the warm sunshine. But he could not see how bright and beautiful it was.

He could hear the birds chirping and singing. But he could not see them as they hopped on the ground or flew in the sky.

How sweet the flowers smelled! But he could not see their bright colors.

He could hear his mother's voice. But he had never seen her kind face.

Then one day the blind man heard the footsteps of many people coming down the road. He was glad. He hoped that some of them would give him money.

The blind man heard people talking about him. Several men said, "Why was this man born blind?" Others said, "Did he or his parents do something wrong?"

They were Jesus' friends, asking Him to explain what they did not understand.

"No," said Jesus. "No one did wrong. He is blind so that God may do a wonderful thing for him."

Jesus knew how very much the blind man wanted to see. He made some soft clay and put it on the man's blind eyes.

Then, Jesus said, "Go wash in the Pool of Siloam."

The blind man wanted to hurry to obey Jesus. But it was hard to find his way to the pool. He had to feel his way slowly.

At last he came to the Pool of Siloam. He splashed the cool water on his eyes until the soft clay was washed away.

"I can see! I can see!" he said.

For the first time he saw the green grass and the blue sky. He saw the birds and the bright flowers.

"How beautiful everything is!" he said, looking around him.

He ran home to tell his mother and father the good news. How fast he could go when he could see the path.

"Jesus made me see," he called to people as he ran.

Some of his neighbors said, "Is this the blind man

who always sat by the road and begged?"

Others said, "He just looks like him."

The happy man said, "I am your neighbor who was blind. A man named Jesus put soft clay on my eyes. He told me to wash in the Pool of Siloam. I washed my eyes and now I can see!"

"How did He ever do it?" asked the people.

"I do not know," said the man. "I only know one thing. I was blind, but now I can see."

After awhile Jesus came to him again.

"Do you believe in the Son of God?" Jesus asked him.

"Who is He, Lord?" asked the man. "If I know, I will believe in Him."

"You have seen Him and are talking to Him now," Jesus said. "I am God's Son."

The man fell down at Jesus' feet. "Lord, I believe in You," he said. "Thank You for making me see."

What a happy man went to his home that night! He told everyone about Jesus, the Son of God, who had made life new for him.

Jesus Dies on the Cross

It was a dark night. Jesus and His friends walked through the quiet city streets. They went out the city gate and crossed a little brook.

Soon they came to a beautiful garden. Taking three of His friends, Jesus went into the garden. "Wait here for me and pray," Jesus said to them.

Then Jesus went off by Himself. He kneeled down and prayed to God. He knew that soon He must die. He asked God to help Him and make Him strong.

All at once, a crowd of noisy men came to the garden. Their lights flashed through the trees. *Clank, clank,* went their swords, *Thud, thud,* went their feet. They talked to each other in loud voices.

"Who are you looking for?" Jesus asked.

"We are looking for Jesus," they said.

"I am Jesus," He told them.

Then the rough soldiers arrested Jesus. They tied His hands and led Him away.

Jesus' friends were afraid. So they ran off. Jesus was left alone with these men who wanted to hurt Him.

They took Jesus to the palace of the High Priest.

"Are You the Christ, the Son of God?" the High Priest asked.

"I am," answered Jesus.

"You could not be!" said the High Priest. He was so angry that he tore his own clothes. "For saying such a terrible thing, You must die."

Early in the morning, the soldiers took Jesus to Pilate, the ruler of the country. Other men who did not like Jesus went with them.

After Pilate talked to Jesus, he said, "This Man has done nothing wrong. He should not have to die."

But the men called out, "Crucify Him! Crucify Him!"

By this time, many other people had come. These people did not like Jesus, either. They shouted, "Crucify Him! Crucify Him!"

Pilate was afraid of the people. "I do not want the blame for killing this good Man," he said.

"We will take the blame," said the people.

So they led Jesus away to be crucified.

Soldiers nailed Jesus to a cross. While He hung there, Jesus looked at the people who wanted to kill Him. He prayed for them. "Father, forgive them. They do not know what they are doing."

Two robbers were being crucified with Jesus. One was sorry that he had done wrong. "Do not forget me," he said to Jesus.

Jesus knew this man had done many bad things.

But He knew that the man was truly sorry for what he had done wrong.

So Jesus told the man, "Today you will be with Me in Heaven."

Jesus saw His mother, Mary, standing nearby. He saw one of His good friends, John, standing near her. He said to John, "Be a son to Mary. Take good care of her."

The sky became very dark. At last Jesus cried out, "It is finished," and He died.

The earth shook. Big rocks broke in pieces. When the captain of the soldiers saw this, he said, "Truly this Man was the Son of God!"

Later some of Jesus' friends came and took Jesus' body. They laid Him in a cave. They rolled a big stone against the door.

Jesus had died. He died for the sins of His people.

Jesus Is Alive Again

Three women walked slowly down a garden path. They were going to the cave where Jesus' body lay. They were very sad because Jesus had died.

It was early in the morning. The birds were singing happy songs. But, Jesus' friends did not listen to the birds. They were too sad.

They wanted to show their love for Jesus. They were taking sweet spices to the cave.

"Who will roll the heavy stone away from the door for us?" asked one of the women.

"There are soldiers watching the cave," said another. "Maybe they will send us away."

All at once, the women stood still. There in front of them was the cave.

"What has happened?" asked one of the women. "The stone has been rolled away!"

"There is not a soldier anywhere!" said another.

They went into the cave. At first they thought it was empty. "Jesus is not here," they said. "Where could He be?"

Then they saw a beautiful shining angel. "Do not be afraid," he said. "Jesus is not here. He is risen.

Go quickly. Tell Jesus' friends that He is alive."

The women ran to the city to tell the good news. But, Jesus' friends did not believe them.

Peter and John hurried to the cave as fast as they could. They wanted to see for themselves if the cave was empty.

John, who was younger, got to the cave first. He looked in. "Jesus is truly gone," he said. Peter went inside the tomb. He saw the cloths that Jesus had been wrapped with lying in the tomb. "Yes, He is gone," said Peter.

The two men walked back to the city. They did not know what to think. "What could have happened to Jesus?" they asked.

Then Mary Magdalene came to the garden alone. She stood crying outside the cave. Jesus had done so many wonderful things for her. How she missed her kind Friend!

Mary looked into the cave. She saw two angels dressed in white. "Woman, why do you cry?" they asked.

"Because someone has taken away my Lord Jesus," said Mary sadly. "And I do not know where He is."

Then Mary turned around. A Man was standing near her. She could not see very well because her eyes were filled with tears. She did not know the Man.

"Why are you crying?" He asked. "Who are you looking for?"

Mary thought he was the man who took care of the garden. "Oh, Sir," she said. "If you have taken Jesus away, tell me where you have laid Him."

Then the Man said to her, "Mary!"

Mary looked at the Man again. She knew that kind voice! It was Jesus!

Mary was so glad to see her good Friend alive again. "My Master!" she cried.

Then Jesus said, "Go to My friends. Tell them that I am alive. Soon I will go to My Father in Heaven."

How happy Mary was as she ran to the city. She hurried to see Jesus' friends. They were still sad and crying because Jesus had died.

"I have good news," said Mary. "I have seen the Lord. He is risen! He talked to me in the garden. Be glad, for Jesus is alive again!"

Paul's Shipwreck

"Good-by. God be with you," called Paul's friends. They stood on the seashore and watched Paul get on the ship. They loved him very much and did not want to say good-by to him.

Paul was a prisoner. He had done nothing wrong. But some people did not want him to tell others about Jesus. So they put him in prison.

Now an army captain was taking Paul across the sea to the big city of Rome. Paul's friends waved as the ship sailed away.

Snap! Flap! The ship's sails blew in the strong wind. The sailors had a hard time sailing the ship. At last they came to an island, where they stopped.

"It is time for bad storms at sea," said Paul. "It is not safe to go on. We must stay here for the winter."

But the sailors would not listen to Paul. The wind was blowing softly, now. So, they sailed the ship out into the sea again.

Soon a strong, high wind began to blow. Angry waves beat against the ship. *Snap! Flap!* The ship's sails blew in the strong, high wind. The sailors could not make the ship go where they wanted it to go. It raced along through the sea.

Creak! Groan! The ship was cracking! The sailors put strong ropes around it to hold it together. They did not want their ship to be wrecked. They threw bundles and jugs over the side to make the ship lighter.

The sky grew very dark. They could not see the sun although it was day time. They could not see at night, either. They did not know where the strong wind was blowing the ship.

The men were afraid that the ship would sink. They thought they would never see land again.

But Paul said, "Do not be afraid. God spoke to me last night. We will lose the ship. But all of us will live."

Still the terrible wind blew. The storm tossed the ship up and down in the sea for two weeks!

Then one night the ship came near land. But the shore was rocky. "We must do something!" cried the sailors. "The ship will be wrecked!"

They dropped four heavy anchors into the sea. They hoped that the anchors would keep the ship away from the rocks.

"It has been two weeks since we have eaten," said Paul. "We need to be strong. Let us all eat. None of you will be hurt."

278

So Paul took some food. He bowed his head and thanked God for it. Then he began to eat. The men were cheered by his words. So they joined him and ate something, too.

When morning came, the strong wind was still blowing. The sailors pulled up the anchors. They tried to land the ship on the beach. But the front part of the ship caught in the mud. Big waves began to break the ship to pieces.

"If you know how to swim," said the captain, "jump into the sea and swim to land. If you cannot swim, take hold of a board and float to shore."

Some of the men swam and some of the men floated on boards.

When the men were out of the sea, the captain counted them. "Everyone is here!" he said.

"We were shipwrecked," said the men. "But all of us are alive. No one is hurt!"

They could hardly believe that they were safe. "God told Paul that we would be safe," they said. "God is very great."

Prayers for Girls and Boys

Time for Prayer

MY HELP

I will look up at the hills,
    my help comes from there.
My help comes from God,
    who made Heaven and earth.
He will not let me fall;
    He will not sleep.
God, who takes care of our country,
    will never sleep.
God takes care of you,
    He will not let anything hurt you
      in the daytime or at night.
God will take care of you
    forever and ever.

GOD MADE THEM ALL

All things bright and beautiful,
    All creatures great and small,
All things wise and wonderful,
    The Lord God made them all.
He gave us eyes to see them,
    And lips that we might tell
How great is God Almighty,
    Who has made all things well.

WE ARE HIS PEOPLE

Make a joyful noise unto the Lord,
    all ye lands.
Serve the Lord with gladness;
    come before His presence with singing.
Know ye that the Lord He is God,
    it is He that hath made us,
    and not we ourselves.
We are His people,
    and the sheep of His pasture.
Enter into His gates with thanksgiving,
    And into His courts with praise.
Be thankful unto Him,
    and bless His name.
For the Lord is good;
    His mercy is everlasting;
And His truth endureth
    to all generations.

—Psalm 100

GREAT AND SMALL

He prayeth best who loveth best
    All things both great and small;
For the dear God who loveth us,
    He made and loveth all.

—S. T. Coleridge

Prayers of Thanks

THANKS BE TO GOD

Thanks be to God
For the good world He has made:
For earth and sea and sky;
For sun and moon and stars;
For daylight and darkness;
For summer and winter;
Seedtime and harvest.

Thanks be to God
For streams of sparkling water;
For wind and rain and snowflakes;
For trees and grass and flowers;
For cattle, sheep, and horses;
For singing birds and
Playful pets.

Thanks be to God
For work and play and worship;
For home, friends, and teachers;
For music, books, and pictures;
For health, joy, and laughter.

Thanks be to God
For the good world He has made.

FOR OUR HOME

O God, our Father,
For our house, our food, our health,
For all who serve our home,
 We thank You.

For making us dear to one another;
For the good times we have together;
For Mother, Father, Brother, Sister,
 We thank You.

That You will help us every day
To show love and kindness to one another,
That each one may think of the other
And be ready to share and help,
 We pray, dear God, our Father.

A GOOD DAY

All day You have been with me, dear God.
You helped me do the things I should,
And let me see the loveliness
Of the deeds of kindness done by others.
For all the gladness and the goodness
That this day has brought,
 I thank You, dear God.

FOR HOME AND FAMILY

For mother love and father care,
For brothers strong and sisters fair,
For love at home and care each day,
For guidance lest we go astray,
  Father in Heaven, we thank Thee.

THE BEAUTY OF LIFE

O God, I thank Thee for each sight
  Of beauty that Thy hand doth give,
For sunny skies, and air, and light;
  O God, I thank Thee that I live.

        —Caroline A. Mason

FOR ALL THY BLESSINGS

We thank Thee, Father, for this day,
For all its work and all its play.
  For school and church so we may learn,
  When we need help, to you we turn.
For home and friends, for rain and sun,
For all thy blessings, every one.

        —Thomas H. Gill

Prayers at Night

MY PRAYER

Now I lay me down to sleep,
I pray dear Lord,
    my soul You'll keep.
May Your love be with me
    through the night,
And bless me with
    the morning light.

DRAW NEAR TO GOD

The whole earth
Is at rest and quiet.
It is good for me
To draw near to God.
I will lie down in peace
    and sleep.

TENDER SHEPHERD

Jesus, tender Shepherd, hear me;
    Bless Thy little lamb tonight:
Through the darkness be Thou near me,
    Keep me safe till morning light.
All this day Thy hand has led me,
    And I thank Thee for Thy care;
Thou hast warmed me, clothed, and fed me;
    Listen to my evening prayer.
Let my sins be all forgiven;
    Bless the friends I love so well:
Take us all at last to heaven,
    Happy there with Thee to dwell.
—Mary Duncan

DAY IS OVER

Now the day is over
    Night is drawing nigh;
Shadows of the evening
    Steal across the sky.
When the morning wakens,
    Then may I arise
Pure, and fresh, and sinless
    In Thy holy eyes.

BEDTIME PRAYER

O God,
I thank Thee for Thy love and care today.
Forgive me if I have done wrong.
Help me always to do right.
Bless my home and all who are in it.
Keep me while I sleep tonight.
And may I always be Thy loving child.

BE KEPT BY THEE

I thank Thee, Lord, that all this day
    Thou hast guided me.
I ask that through this night I may
    Still be kept by Thee.

MY EVENING PRAYER

Dear God, hear my evening prayer:
I thank You for Your love and care,
    I thank You for this happy day,
    For home and friends, for work and play.
Bless the ones I love tonight,
And keep us all till morning light.

Grace Before Meals

A GRATEFUL HEART

We thank Thee, Lord, that thou dost give
Our daily food that we may live.
Wilt thou to each this gift impart:
A loving and a grateful heart.

THE EYES OF ALL

The eyes of all
Wait upon thee, O Lord:
> And thou giveth them meat
> In due season.
Bless, O Lord, this food to our use,
And us to thy service,
And make us ever mindful
Of the needs of others.

GOD'S GOODNESS

Let me know Your goodness, God,
As I eat my daily food;
Let me feel Your love
As I enjoy my world.

WE THANK THEE

Dear Lord, we thank Thee for Thy care,
> And all Thy mercy sends;
For food we eat, the clothes we wear,
> Our health and home and friends.

Prayers in the Morning

RIGHT IN YOUR EYES

O God, who has brought us
To the beginning of this day,
Grant that this day
We fall into no sin,
Neither run into
Any kind of danger;
But that all our doing
May be right in Your eyes.

THE DAY SO FAIR

Father, we thank Thee for the night,
And for the pleasant morning light;
    For rest and food and loving care,
    And all that makes the day so fair.
Help us to do the things we should,
To be to others kind and good;
    In all we do at work or play
    To grow more loving ev'ry day.

—Rebecca J. Weston

LOVELY THOUGHTS

The world is very still, dear God;
    I'd like to softly pray;
I have some lovely thoughts of You,
    But thoughts are hard to say.
Yet You can even hear my thoughts—
    The thoughts I cannot say—
And You can love a boy or girl
    Who finds this way to pray.

PLEASING TO YOU

Let all the words I say,
And all the thoughts of my heart,
Be pleasing to You,
This day, dear God.

BLESS ME THIS DAY

God bless me this day.
Help me to be obedient and kind.
Give me a loving heart and helpful hands,
    that I may be willing and able
    to do what is right,
    and be happy doing it.

THIS NEW DAY

Thank You, dear God,
For this new day;
For its gladness
And its brightness;
For the long hours
Waiting to be filled with
Happy play and useful work.
Thank You, dear God,
For this new day.

HELP ME O GOD

Help me, O God, throughout this day,
That in my work and in my play
My thoughts and words and deeds may be
Controlled and guided, Lord, by Thee.

IN THE MORNING

In the morning
I will look up to God.
God will hear me when I pray unto Him.
God will show me what is good,
And will put gladness into my heart.

Prayers for Others

FOR OTHER CHILDREN

Our loving Heavenly Father,
    Now hear us as we pray
For all the other children
    Both near and far away.
We ask Thee for Thy blessing
    For each one every day:
Help us to love each other,
    And for each other pray.

FOR THE SICK

O God, who loves all people,
We pray for those who are sick.
Fill the doctors with wisdom
And make them skillful.
Let all the sick people,
And all who take care of them,
Feel your love about them.
Let them know of the love and thought
Of all who know them
And want to help them.
O God, who loves all people,
Help those who are sick.

Prayers for Myself

GOD BE WITH ME EVERY DAY

God be with me every day,
When I work and when I play;
    When I read and when I talk;
    When I ride and when I walk;
When I laugh and when I cry,
God forever be nearby.

THIS HEART OF MINE

Jesus take this heart of mine
Make it pure and only Thine;
    I thy loving child would be,
    Help me Lord to live for Thee.

FOR THREE THINGS I PRAY

Dear Lord, for these three things
    I pray:
    To know Thee more clearly,
    To love Thee more dearly,
    To follow Thee more nearly,
Every day.

HELP ME TO REMEMBER

Help me, dear God, to remember
That I am Your child,
And belong to You.
Help me to love others
As You have loved me.
Help me to be generous and kind,
Truthful in what I say,
And kind to those about me.
Speak to my mind,
That I may know You;
Speak to my heart,
That I may love You;
Speak to my body, that it may do
What You would have me do.

WITH THEE

Be with me, Lord Jesus:
    I ask Thee to stay
Close by me forever,
    And love me I pray.
Bless all the dear children
    In Thy tender care,
And fit us for Heaven
    To live with Thee there.

— *Martin Luther*

Special Prayers

LET ME BE GLAD

Whether You send sunshine
Or whether You send rain,
Let me be glad, dear God,
And trust Your love.

TEACH ME LORD

Lord, I pray Thee,
Teach me to think of Thee
    and to love Thee every day that I live;
To know Jesus, my Savior,
    and what He has done for me,
    how good He is to me,
    and how He can help me.
May I look into my heart
To see if there is anything wicked there;
    and may I put away from me
    everything that is bad
    and resist those who would teach me evil.
Bless my church and Sunday school,
    my parents who love me, my teachers,
And all who are working for Thy Kingdom.

LOVE AND KINDNESS

Help me, O God,
    to be loving and forgiving.
May I not think unkind thoughts
    about other people,
    or say unkind words to them.
May I remember how Jesus loved
    even those who hated Him,
and may I try to be like Jesus every day.